M000011985

A Glass Full of Tears

Dementia Day-by-Day

June Lund Shiplett

Foreword by David S. Geldmacher, M.D.

Writer's World Press
Cleveland, Ohio

Writer's World Press, P.O. Box 24684
Cleveland, Ohio 44124-0684, U.S.A.
Telephone: 216/481-1974

This book recounts one person's experience with a medical situation and a physician's response to that specific situation. It is not intended as, and should not be used as, a substitute for medical advice from a licensed professional. The reader should consult a physician in matters relating to his/her health or the health of others and particularly to any symptoms that may require diagnosis or medical attention. Every effort has been made to make this book as accurate as possible. The author and publisher assume no responsibility for errors, inaccuracies, omissions, or any inconsistency herein.

First Edition Softbound

10 9 8 7 6 5 4 3 2 1

Preassigned LCCN: 96-60203

Publisher's Cataloging in Publication

Shiplett, June Lund.
A glass full of tears: dementia day-by-day/ June Lund Shiplett; foreword by David S. Geldmacher.
p. cm.
Includes bibliographical references.
ISBN 0-9631441-2-X

1. Dementia--patients--Case studies. 1. Dementia--Patients--Home care--Psychological aspects. 3. Dementia--Patients--Family relationships. 4. Caregivers--Psychology. I. Title.

RC521.S45 1996 616.8'3
QB196-20254

For my husband, Charlie,
and all those like him
who suffer from
dementia
and
their caregivers

May God bless you
and give you
peace some day

For Pattie – Thanks for being such a nice person – As a caregiver you know where I'm coming from – Bless you

Your friend [illegible]

Oct 26, 1996

CONTENTS

FOREWORD

Dementia. It is a distancing, impersonal word. Perhaps we in the health care professions prefer it that way. The word represents something that the doctor's or nurse's training and practice allows them to understand only in the abstract. In contrast, June Shiplett's diary recounts her husband's journey into that illness and vividly demonstrates the uncomfortably close and intensely personal human experiences of dementia. Many of this book's readers will be caregivers for demented individuals and have already found these things out for themselves, but it is my hope that health care providers will gain new insight in these pages about the experiences of the people and families affected by dementia.

Dementia is an old word. It entered medical English in the early nineteenth century as another word for insanity, and variants of the word, in one form or another, date back to the 1500s. Indeed, paralleling everyday American English, the word literally means "out of one's mind." In current medical use, dementia means something different from "crazy." Formally, dementia is defined as loss in memory and other intellectual abilities, often accompanied by changes in personality, severe enough to interfere with a person's previous ability to function in everyday life. Thus, it is a description, rather than a disease (or what doctors would call a specific diagnosis). It does not imply any exact cause. The real key is the person's loss of ability to function in his or her own established way of life.

Declines in intellectual abilities in later life have been recognized for centuries. Words other than dementia, however, have been used to describe these changes. Senility is one of the older and more common; it means "an aged state." The health care professions have moved away from the use of "senile" or "senility" to describe severe changes in intellect because we recognize that disease, rather than age, is the most important contributor to loss of function in later life. Most people these days know a person in their eighties or nineties whose intellect is intact (the phrase "sharp as a tack" seems universal). Unfortunately, in my practice, I also treat many people in their fifties and sixties with severe intellectual impairments. Since "senile" is another way of saying aged, it really empahsizes the wrong thing about memory loss. This distinction is also important because memory loss severe enough to interfere with everyday life, *at any age*, should be evaluated by a doctor or nurse practitioner. Age, by itself, is not enough to cause disabling mental impairments.

"Hardening of the arteries" is another old term. It came about when medical science believed that a chronic, gradual loss of blood supply to the brain was the cause of memory loss and behavior change in the elderly. It is clear that strokes and hemorrhages, like the ones Charlie Shiplett had, can lead to impairments, but the blood supply to the brain is adequate in a large proportion of people with dementia. "Organic brain syndrome" is another problem term. When looked at closely, it just doesn't mean much. Some health care providers will use it to indicate that a brain illness, rather than a psychiatric disease like schizophrenia or manic-depression, is the source of mental symptoms—but it doesn't say which brain disease or why. Dementia is historically correct, more clearly defined, and more concise.

While more than sixty diseases have been identified to cause dementia, those illnesses share many of the same symptoms. Readers of this book will see the most common ones. Memory loss is fundamental, but complex. It is confusing to many families that old memories should be so well preserved, but new ones lost. If the memory loss is viewed as a failure to store memories properly and efficiently, then the range of memory difficulties and some of their variability becomes easier to understand. Another very common part of memory loss is unawareness of the problem, which differs from psychological denial. I often describe this as the affected person's forgetting *that* they forget. Changes in personality, ranging from progressive timidity to frank belligerence are typical, too. Studies show that the personality changes and other non-intellectual symptoms like agitation, apathy, delusions, hallucinations, and day-night reversals are far more troubling to caregivers than the cognitive decline. In 1996, our treatment of these kinds of symptoms remains problematic. While early steps and promising developments are occurring, there is no medicine or other tonic which will restore memory or personality to their previous states. We can reduce adverse behaviors, but often at the cost of side effects. Our medicines do not know the difference between good behavior and bad, so reducing the bad behaviors frequently leads to reduction in normal activity as well.

The problems encountered by the Shipletts were the result of multi-infarct dementia. Charlie's dementia was caused by multiple bleeding strokes (hemorrhages) which destroyed portions of the brain responsible for memory and behavior. This is a far less common cause of dementia than Alzheimer's disease, which may affect up to four million Americans today and is expected to triple over the next fifty years. Nonetheless, Charlie and June's experiences are not unlike those of most families facing dementia, regardless of cause. They can teach a valuable lesson to all of us who work and live with dementia and the people affected by it.

DAVID S. GELDMACHER, M.D.
Clinical Director,
University Alzheimer Center
University Hospitals of Cleveland
Assistant Professor of Neurology
Case Western Reserve University

AUTHOR'S NOTE

This is a journal I kept while on a journey with my husband, Charlie, through the ravages of a disease called multi-infarct dementia. I started it because I didn't know what was happening to us and felt that I should have a record, maybe something to tell the doctors, should the need arise. After Charlie was diagnosed, I kept writing it for myself because by putting it all down on paper, I was able to purge my heart from the terror of it all.

I realize now that we all have burdens in life to either accept or reject. It's not the burdens we have that count, but how we face them. We can square our shoulders, stick out our chins and keep going, or we can sit down, give up and become a basket case ourselves. It's whatever way we choose. And I think the best way is to stick out your chin, keep your faith, and a heart full of love. I learned that I'm stronger than I thought I was and that love is one of the strongest emotions we have as human beings. Love is not just wanting to be with someone all the time, and it isn't just the physical excitement and touching, it's sharing who and what you are with that other person. It's giving yourself unconditionally, without thought to reward. It's hanging on when you don't think you can possibly hang on any longer.

And yet that's where I made another mistake. I held onto Charlie too long and I hope anyone reading this journal will learn by my mistake. I should have let go of him much sooner than I did because by the time I finally let go, he wasn't really my Charlie anymore. Please, don't do what I did. If you have a loved one who has dementia, don't keep them at home with you until they begin to destroy you. And being a caregiver can destroy you if you let it.

As I look back, I realize that I made many mistakes. Some were the times when I doubted that God was with me, other times were when I thought what was happening to us was our fault because of something we might have done. I know now that God didn't do this to Charlie and me, and we didn't do it to ourselves either, it's just something that happened.

I think we all have a tendency to dislike failure, and I think that's what I was afraid of doing, failing. Failing Charlie when I felt he needed me the most. Now, I understand that letting go of him wasn't failing him. I had to let go of him in order to keep on loving him because the horror I was going through was slowly destroying that love. When every day becomes a battle just to survive, let go. When you realize you're losing your own identity, let go. When the doctors tell you that it's time, don't fight them, let go. I didn't fail Charlie, but I almost failed myself because I didn't want to accept life without him.

Now to the most important reason I kept this journal. During this devastating time in my life, I was unable to find a book written by someone who had faced a similar situation alone twenty-four hours a day, seven days a week, the way I had. Therefore, I thought I could share my story. I know there are others who are going through what I went through. If knowing you're not alone and learning from my mistakes will help even one of you survive, then keeping and sharing this journal was worth it.

JUNE LUND SHIPLETT

ACKNOWLEDGMENTS

Many times we face a crisis in our lives thinking we're alone but later when we look back on it, we realize that there were others without whose help we couldn't have made it. I thank God for giving me the strength to get through this difficult time in my life, and for providing me with the loving support of my family, neighbors, and friends.

A *great big thank you* goes to my family, especially my children, who were understanding, and never complained when I cried on their shoulders.

Special recognition goes to my daughter, Yvonne Shiplett, who was always there when I needed her no matter what hour of the day or night. She and her son, Braxton, were so good with my husband, that I never had to worry when I left Charlie with them in order to be able to get some much needed time alone. I could never have gone through those years without her.

I thank my oldest daughter, Maureen Allen, for her unselfish sharing of her husband, Jim, who did many of the things around the house that Charlie used to do. And to Jim, for being the son we never had. I know there were many times when he could have been doing other, more enjoyable things. He gave of his time when I needed him, and he made it sound like he was having fun.

Special thanks goes to my daughter, Geraldine (Jill) Piet, for those Wednesdays spent with her father and for her beautiful illustration that appears in this book. She knew the significance of the robin's nest to my survival.

Thanks goes to my daughter Laura Campbell whose frequent phone calls and letters from Florida brightened days when I felt as if the world had forgotten me.

A big thank you also goes to Dr. David Geldmacher and his staff at the Foley Elder Care Center, who, no matter when or how many times I called, never made me feel I was a nuisance. They helped me understand that I didn't have to hate myself for the feelings that sometimes overwhelmed me.

To my neighbor Carol Cederlund and her son, Roy, the words "thank you" seem so inadequate because their help meant so much. Carol was there so many times to help me pick up the pieces and get through to Charlie when I was at my wits end. She and Roy willingly gave of themselves, asking nothing in return. I am truly blessed to have such neighbors who care and continue to show their concern.

I also want to thank the Reverend Shirley Malzer, Reverend Charlotte Brown and the congregation of the First Congregational Church in Fairport Harbor, OH, whose prayers gave me strength when I thought I wouldn't make it through another day.

To my author friends, my many devoted fans, and all the members of Northeast Ohio Romance Writers of America, bless you for taking the time to stay in touch, and offering encouragement when my spirits were at an all time low.

A special thank you also goes to Raffey Severino and the members of my Alzheimer's support group who helped me understand that I was not alone, and that there was a place I could go for help. I needed you all then, and still do.

My last thank you goes to Lavern Hall, my editor and publisher, who had faith in me as a writer, and believed my story needed to be told. Her editing skills were invaluable as we faced the monumental task of turning a ten year journal into a book. She preserved my husband's dignity while helping others understand that multi-infarct dementia, like Alzheimer's, is a devastating disease that in destroying the brain, destroys the person in the process. Thank you Lavern for everything.

1

“In The Beginning”

June 17, 1983

Charlie forgot my birthday. In all the forty-three years we’ve been married Charlie has never forgotten my birthday, Sweetest Day, Valentine’s Day, or any other holiday. He would give me a gift along with the biggest, most romantic card lovingly signed. But today, my birthday went unnoticed.

June 23

Charlie’s birthday. I gave him the card and gift I bought him weeks ago, setting them on his plate at the supper table.

“What’s this?” he asked as we both sat down to eat.

“It’s your birthday,” I told him. “I got you a present.”

“A present?” he shouted. “What are you trying to do, make me feel guilty for forgetting your birthday?”

“Don’t be ridiculous,” I said. “I always get you something for your birthday. You know that.”

"Well, I don't want it," he yelled. "You can take it and shove it!" and he threw the unopened gift across the table.

I'm so hurt. This isn't like Charlie. He refused to even read the card. I feel terrible!

July 15

Charlie talks all the time these days about one of the women he works with at the shop.

"Boy, you ought to see what she can do," he said at dinner. "She works on cars, loves tractor pulls and even car races." He sounds exactly like a boy who had suddenly discovered girls.

"Are you spending your rest periods and lunch hours with her?" I finally got enough courage to ask him one day.

"So what if I am," he answered. "I'm not doing anything wrong. I'm just being friendly, that's all."

July 21

Charlie drives a tow motor in the shop and over the years I've heard him talk about some of the dispatchers and other women he works with, but this seems to be different. Whenever he talks about this woman there's something in his voice and the things he says don't seem to come across as being mere friendship.

Every time I question him about it, or try to find out just what is going on, he becomes furious and acts as if I have no right to even mention it to him or question him in any way. He even came right out and said, "It's none of your damn business what I do at work."

August 8

I'm worried. This isn't my warm, loving Charlie. Not the man I've always known. How many times I've heard about women whose husbands suddenly leave them for a younger woman. And this woman is much younger than I am by about twenty years. I saw her today when one of our cars wasn't working and I had to pick Charlie up from work. How strange. She reminds me very much of what I looked like when I was her age.

August 10

People laugh about men and their mid-life crisis, but it's nothing to laugh about. I am so afraid that something like this is happening to him and there's nothing I can do to stop it. I'm afraid people are going to start talking. I know Charlie comes right home to me on time every night after work, but the people at the shop don't, and it hurts me knowing that they might think Charlie is seeing her away from the shop. I feel betrayed.

August 12

I finally came right out last night and told Charlie I don't want him to spend his rest periods with that woman anymore, or eat lunch with her, or walk her to her car because of what people would think. He flatly refused. I cried myself to sleep. But he didn't even seem to care. He was so cold, unfeeling, and indifferent to anything I said or did. This morning he acts as if nothing ever happened.

September 15

One of the men Charlie works with was killed in an auto accident, and Charlie and I planned to go to the funeral parlor tonight. He was going to come home from work, change clothes and we'd ride back in to town.

Around noon today, the phone rang and it was Charlie calling on his lunch break. "You know, I was thinking," he said. "If you don't care, I think I'll go to the funeral parlor right after work instead of this evening. What do you think?"

"I think we should go tonight," I told him.

"But that would mean we'd have to make another trip all the way in here. The funeral parlor's right around the corner from work." He sounded irritated.

"It's not all that far," I told him.

"But all the guys are going right after work and I think I ought to go with them."

He was starting to get angry because I was insisting that it would be better if we both paid our respects, so I finally said, "All right then, go ahead with the guys."

After I hung up the phone I got to thinking, and the more I thought about it, the more I realized that most of the arguments Charlie gave for me not going just didn't make any sense. The suspicions began. By the time he got home late this afternoon, I confronted him.

"You went to the funeral parlor with that woman, didn't you?" I said.

His face reddened. "So what if I did."

"Just the two of you alone in our car, am I right?"

"That's right," he answered. "So what's it to you?"

I wanted to hit him, do something to make him hurt like I was hurting. But all I did was try to hold back the tears, then I turned and walked away. There has never been a time in my life when I felt so lost and alone.

November 8

Tonight when we were out riding in the car, Charlie and I started arguing over a math problem as we talked about the household bills. He tried to tell me one thing but it was so obvious his answer was wrong, I was astounded. Charlie has always been good at math, but tonight it was as if he had no concept of what I was talking about.

Although he has only been through eight grades of school in a one room schoolhouse in southern Ohio, most people who meet him think he has graduated from college. In fact, he is a very smart man because he reads a great deal and is self taught.

Some years ago, he decided that he wanted to be a millwright, but discovered that in order to do so, he needed to take a test with algebra. He hardly even knew what algebra was, but did he give up? No. He went to the library and took out a book about algebra and taught himself enough to pass the test. Unfortunately, he ended up going back on the tow motor because he was allergic to dust.

* * *

December 20, 1984

Charlie is getting forgetful and irritable, and our sex life has begun to suffer. Sometimes he's unable to perform. At first, I thought it was my fault because I'm not slim and attractive anymore, but that never bothered him before. Our love life has always been full and satisfying, but now it is almost nonexistent. When I tried to get him to go to the doctor to find out what's wrong he wouldn't have any part of it.

* * *

June 18, 1985

It feels like I'm living with a stranger. Charlie treats me more like a housekeeper than a wife! He never comes up behind me and puts his arms around me anymore, and he just doesn't seem to want me around when he's doing anything. This is strange because he used to ask me to sit by him when he was working outside so we could talk.

September 8

Finally, after two years of putting up with his constantly talking about that other woman, I decided to give him an ultimatum. Either he stops talking to her or I'm leaving him.

When we went out for a drive this afternoon, everything I was going to say to him kept running through my mind. I told myself I'd give him one last chance. If he didn't agree to stop being friends with her, I'd give him the ultimatum.

When we pulled into our driveway, I asked him to please stop spending time with her, expecting to get the same stubborn answer. Instead, he looked over at me and said, "You know, you're right." He not only agreed to stop spending time with her, but said he'd tell her that he didn't think it looked right because people were going to start gossiping.

I don't know what to think. I can't believe what I heard. I have no idea why he suddenly changed his mind.

September 11

Charlie's relationship with that other woman has ended. I can't explain it or even make sense out of it, but I don't care. I'm relieved!

This has been a terrible time for me emotionally and one that will be hard for me to forget. But since that afternoon when he agreed with me, it's like a miracle happened. Once more he's the warm affectionate man I've always known.

September 16

I've been thinking about Charlie today. For a man in his sixties, he's still a handsome fella. He has a full head of ebony hair, although his sideburns are frosted now, and his features are classic. His dark brown eyes crinkle in the corners when he's teasing and thinks he's being cute, his big dimples dent his cheeks when he laughs, which is often, and he has the broadest shoulders I've ever seen on a man who's only five feet eight. His hands are big, too, strong but so gentle. As gentle as his heart. There's nothing he wouldn't do for others. He's always loved people. He talks to everyone in the cashier's line at the supermarket as if they were his neighbor.

He wasn't always so outgoing. When we got married January 7th, 1950, Charlie was quite shy. Maybe it was from being brought up on a farm in the southern part of Ohio, or from being the middle child in a family of twelve children. Except for a stint in the army, when he was stationed in Germany as a military policeman at eighteen, he really didn't see much of the world. His life was almost all work. His father had died in a car accident when Charlie was sixteen, and he worked in factories to help support his brothers and sisters. He didn't even like to eat out because he was embarrassed to eat in front of people.

Over the years, I've seen this shy, self-conscious man come out of his shell. Since I wrote and published my first book at age forty-eight, and through the fifteen years and fifteen published novels since, Charlie has just blossomed.

Every time we go to a writer's conference, luncheon, or autograph session he seems to be in his glory, talking with all the authors, and telling them how proud he is of me and my success. I couldn't have a bigger fan or a better publicity agent. He gets along with everyone too, and often tells people that romance writers are the nicest people in the world.

All his life Charlie has been the kind of person who gave himself to others. He helped people no matter what the problem and he treated everyone with warmth and kindness.

Back in the seventies when Charlie's mother was in a nursing home about fifty miles away, he went to see her often, even in bad weather. If one of his relatives was sick, or in the hospital, Charlie was right there to cheer them up.

For years, Charlie cut the grass for the widow who lived next door. When the elderly lady across the street became housebound, he helped her all he could. Later, when she went into a nursing home, he visited her every week. Charlie would read to her, feed her ice cream, and he never expected a thing in return. Charlie used to say, "Just to see a smile on her face was thanks enough." And this was when he was in his late thirties, a time when most men are more interested in hunting, fishing, and sports rather than being compassionate.

To me, Charlie had an uncanny way of caring for the elderly and the sick. I always told him that he would have made a marvelous doctor because of his bedside manner.

September 17

After writing so much about Charlie yesterday, I thought I'd write about me today. I guess I'm just not what most people think of when they think of a novelist. I could never play the lead role on *Murder She Wrote*. I'm too short, too overweight, and could never do most of the things Jessica Fletcher does. Every time I try to act reserved and sophisticated, the way most people think writers are, it never comes across. I guess I'm just too down to earth.

Although I'm the mother of four daughters, Maureen, Jill, Yvonne and Laura, and a grandmother of five, my hair is not gray yet. It's still brown, heavily frosted at the temples. My hazel eyes are usually hidden behind half glasses that drive most people crazy when they're perched on my nose.

My girls always kid me and say I've had three careers. Before I married Charlie, I was a switchboard operator for Ohio Bell and sang with a local dance band on weekends. After marrying Charlie, I became a homemaker and mother. Now I'm a novelist. I *love* writing—and everything that goes with it.

September 20

Today Charlie and I were talking about how much things have changed. Our house used to be a cottage when Mentor-on-the-Lake, Ohio was a resort town. Now, however, the cottages are year round houses. The dance hall where the big bands used to play has been torn down, and what was once a midway, when Charlie and I were courting back in the late forties, is now the main thoroughfare, with a couple of drive-ins, a supermarket, gas station, a few taverns, a church, the town hall, and police and fire station. We're the third house from the end of a dead end street, and all that separates our house from Lake Erie is a marshy lagoon and a sandbar. We've lived here since November of 1954 and if we ever had to move, it would break our hearts.

October 16

Charlie's been more loving and attentive to me lately, but he's also getting more forgetful. Tonight, he checked the oil in the car. He discovered the hood was up when he happened to glance out the window and saw snow falling on the motor. He's been mislaying things or starting out to get something and forgetting what he wants.

These are the kinds of things that remind me of that spring morning a couple years ago, when I looked out in the backyard and saw all of his tools right on the picnic table where he'd left them the night before. Then about a week later, he left the extension cord stretched from the tool shed 250 feet across the lawn. Charlie has never been careless. He's always been a workaholic and there's nothing he can't fix, from furnaces to cars, and to him, his tools are the most precious things next to his family.

Today, he can't seem to work the VCR or make sense out of the TV guide, but he can figure out the microwave oven. Is it old age creeping up? Everyone I've talked to says, "Oh, hey, I forget things all the time too."

November 1

Charlie retired from the shop after almost thirty-five years of service. His last day of work was spent saying good-bye to everyone. He says he's going to miss the many friends he has made over the years.

I am happy for Charlie. All he's ever talked about was the day he could retire. Charlie said, "retirement means going fishing whenever I want, puttering around the house, building things with my electric saw, and just enjoying life."

* * *

December 23, 1991

The last few years have just seemed to fly by with all the writing conferences, autograph sessions and books being published. My latest book, *Boston Renegade* is due for release in August of 1992, and I have started working on another book I titled, *A Bridge Too Far To Cross*. I have been wanting to write it for years. It's a love story between a woman who isn't Amish and an Amishman. It is my first attempt at a mainstream book.

Charlie is enjoying his retirement. He and the neighbor who lives across the street and is eighty-four years young, take a two mile walk almost every day, weather permitting. Charlie looks forward to his walks and loves to stop at the drive-in for a cup of coffee before heading back home.

He goes fishing with his older brother, is getting to know his grandchildren better, and our marriage is back to normal. We are both happier than we have ever been.

In February, I am scheduled to do a writer's workshop at the "Fun In the Sun" Romance Writer's Conference in Fort Lauderdale, Florida. Charlie and I are delighted because our daughter, Laura, and her husband Tom, live in Pompano Beach, just outside of Fort Lauderdale, and it will give us a chance to see their home.

Laura is our youngest daughter and one of the brunettes. Two of our daughters are blondes and two are brunettes and when you see all four girls together it's really hard to believe they're sisters.

I remember when Laura met Tom. She was working at a local bookstore. Laura said Tom used the oldest line in the book to meet her, when he walked up to her and said, "Say, don't I know you from somewhere?"

They dated for a year, were engaged for almost four years, and set the wedding date for May of 1988. However,

Tom was laid off from his job in March of 1988, and they thought they'd have to call off the wedding. Fortunately, one of Laura's girlfriends wrote to her and told her they should move to Florida where jobs for accountants were plentiful. So Tom and Laura decided to get married in March and head south. Tom got a job right away at a bank and Laura now works for the *Sun Sentinel.*

They raise cats and already have four. Whenever we get a card from them they always sign it, Laura, Tom and the "Kids," and they put a bunch of paw prints on the page. Charlie and I always get a big kick out of it.

2
"The Incident"

January 10, 1992

Charlie is a little upset with me this morning because I am going to take our granddaughter Brittany, to the doctors. Our oldest daughter Maureen, her husband, Jim, daughter Brittany, and son Grant, live about twenty minutes from us and Maureen always makes appointments for Brittany, then asks me to take her. Charlie says it's not right. He says Maureen is taking advantage of me. I try to make him understand that I don't really mind because it gives me a chance to spend some time with my granddaughter. At sixteen, she's always so busy with her school work and friends that I rarely get to see her. To me it isn't a chore, but a pleasure. Charlie just doesn't see it that way.

Just before I left, our daughter, Yvonne, came over to wash clothes. Yvonne's a single parent and she and her son, Braxton, who is almost ten, live in an apartment complex about fifteen minutes from our house. She does her wash here every week.

Yvonne is the next to youngest and is one of the blondes. When she was little, her hair was so blonde that it was almost white, and her eyes were the brightest blue, just like the sky on a summer day. When she turned twelve, her hair started to turn a darker golden color and her eyes began to turn green. Now her eyes are as green as the eyes of a cat and her hair's the color of burnt honey

Anyway, when I left, everything was just fine. Charlie was busy puttering around the house, and Yvonne was taking care of her wash. I was gone most of the afternoon and didn't get back until around four o'clock, right when Yvonne was leaving.

When I got out of the car I asked, "How is everything?"

"Fine," she said. "Except I think maybe dad's still a little peeved with you for going because he's been awfully quiet the last couple of hours."

I smiled and got a warm smile back. After saying good-bye, I went into the house. Since I was planning to make homemade chicken noodle soup for supper, I decided to start on it right away. Charlie was putting some dirty dishes into the dishwasher.

I said "Hi" and shooed him into the other room to watch his favorite nature program. In our pullman kitchen there's really only room for one person at a time.

Once I got the chicken in the pot with the onions and celery, I joined Charlie in the living room. We watched the wildlife show together. He didn't really talk to me.

When the chicken was done, I took it out to cool, so I could take the meat off the bones. While it was cooling, I told Charlie I was going to lie down because I was tired.

He said, "Okay," so I went into the bedroom. When I came out fifteen minutes later he was still watching the program, so I got supper ready. After setting the table I called him over to eat and we sat down. Usually when I fix chicken noodle soup Charlie says "Boy, this is so good I could hurt myself," or "You know, you ought to have this stuff canned and sell it." Tonight, he was awfully quiet and just sat there eating.

After supper, I cleared away the dishes, put them in the dishwasher and got it started. Charlie was still sitting at the table. He looked lost and forlorn so I asked him if he'd like to play pinochle.

He said, "Okay."

Charlie has always been good at pinochle. The first hand, I got the bid. Charlie kept playing cards he should never have played. Each time he did, I glanced at him, but I didn't say anything.

Right in the middle of the second hand, he suddenly threw his cards on the table and yelled, "I can't! I can't!"

I tried to find out what was the matter, but he couldn't talk. He got up from the table and came over by me. He'd start to say something, get two words out, then just stood there staring at me with a wild, scared look in his eyes.

I was petrified and shaking all over. My first thought was to call the rescue squad, only when I started to pick up the phone he grabbed my hand and wouldn't let me.

"No! I'm all right," he said.

"But you're not all right," I said. There's something wrong."

He kept repeating that he was all right over and over again. I pleaded with him for the next couple of hours to let me do something. I wanted to take him to the emergency room at the hospital, but he'd have no part of that either. Every time I mentioned the hospital or the rescue squad, he'd get angry and upset. I didn't know what to do. I was really frightened.

By almost 10:00 p.m., he had calmed down. He went into the bathroom, grabbed his pajama bottoms and said,

"Bed." So we got ready for bed. I made him promise me that if he was still having problems in the morning, he'd go see the doctor.

After tucking him in his bed, I went to my own bedroom so my snoring wouldn't keep him awake. Charlie went right to sleep, but not me. I cried and prayed until sleep came.

January 11

This morning, Charlie was still unable to say more than a few words. In spite of the fact that he agreed to see a doctor if he wasn't any better, he rebelled against going. I told him either he goes to the doctor's office, or I'll call the rescue squad. He finally gave in, and after quickly downing breakfast, we headed for the clinic.

Dr. Stoerkel, our family doctor, was on duty at the Madison Clinic Emergency Room. After examining Charlie, Dr. Stoerkel immediately sent us to the hospital in Painesville, Ohio, where Charlie was admitted.

While Charlie was undergoing CAT scans and all sorts of tests, I called the girls. They came to the hospital right away but there was really nothing we could do.

This evening I am in such turmoil. I have no idea what is going on except that Charlie is in trouble.

January 12

It's Sunday. The hospital neurologist told me that Charlie has had a cerebral hemorrhage. He said the bleeding had stopped, but the damage was already done. He also said that even if I had brought Charlie to the hospital Friday night it wouldn't have helped.

The neurologist told me that Charlie has scar tissue on his brain from having, what he called "infarcts", some years before. He explained that there are different types of infarcts associated with the brain and the type of infarct Charlie has is when a blood vessel ruptures sending blood directly into the brain damaging it. He said it probably would have changed Charlie's personality for awhile before it healed, and would have taken about two years to heal. The neurologist then asked me if I knew when that might have been.

Well, confronted with this, I told the doctor about some of the things that went on between spring 1983 and late summer 1985. He agreed that Charlie must have had those small infarcts then. The infarcts weren't like what he had now, but were bad enough to change his personality for awhile. Once the infarcts healed, Charlie reverted back to the way he had been before, leaving only slight damage that caused the forgetfulness he's had at times, and his inability to make sense out of the TV guide, or use the VCR.

Finally, I have an answer to what has puzzled me for so long. It wasn't me back in 1983, and it wasn't him. His behavior was caused by something physical that neither of us could control.

After the conversation with the doctor today, I suddenly began to realize the trouble we're in. Although Charlie knows who I am, where he lives, how long we've been married, he has no idea where he is, or what is happening, and he can say only one or two words at the most.

I am devastated! I feel like my whole world is falling apart. I have always been able to cope with death and physical ailments, but how am I going to cope with something like this? This was my husband, a man who had always been vitally alive and now he is suddenly reduced to depending on others for everything. The thought that he might never remember how to do anything again is terrifying.

January 17

Today Charlie was discharged from the hospital under Dr. Stoerkel's care. He is still only using one or two words at a time. He can't read or write his name. He says the TV drives him to distraction. The words are all mixed up to him. He can't use the microwave either.

February 12

We're trying to cope as best we can. The doctor has Charlie taking Diazepam, to help keep him calmed down, Zoloft so he won't get depressed and Dilantin so he won't have any seizures. Taking care of him is like taking care of a two year old, except he's a man, in a man's body. I have to do almost everything for him. Help him eat, help him dress, help him use the bathroom. Sometimes he comes over to where I'm sitting in the chair in the evening. He kneels down beside it and wants to know what's the matter. He knows something is wrong, but he is all mixed up about everything. I tell him the truth. That he has some brain damage and that the doctor said with time it will probably heal. It doesn't help much because he can't seem to grasp what I am saying.

February 27

Dr. Stoerkel sent us to a neurologist to have an angiogram done of Charlie's brain. After taking the angiogram, we were told that Charlie was lucky to be alive. The neurologist said that by all rights Charlie should have died, but somehow, for some reason, and they don't really know why, his body compensated for the hemorrhaging. I wonder how long it will take to heal and what damage will be left behind.

March 12

The MRI Charlie had last week showed no new bleeding. It's taken a lot of prayers and patience and Charlie has finally begun to heal.

April 13

Charlie is talking in sentences again. He can use the microwave and he's back to making coffee every morning. He's still extremely forgetful, and often gets confused when I try to explain things to him, but all in all he seems to be doing quite well.

June 19

Charlie is back to taking his two and a half mile walks again every day with the neighbor across the street. He's even put a fuel pump in one of the cars and a battery in the other. He is beginning to enjoy life again.

July 24

Good news. Charlie's allowed to start driving again! It gives him back a sense of independence. Now he can run errands and I'm free to write. Everyone, including Dr. Stoerkel, is amazed at his progress.

August 25

It's been over six months since the cerebral hemorrhage and Charlie hasn't had any seizures so the doctor discontinued the Dilantin.

September 8

There are subtle changes coming over Charlie. He seems to be getting more forgetful, and gets more easily confused. Maybe it's just my imagination. Maybe I'm paying too much attention to everything he says and does. That can happen when you worry about someone. I'm going to try to stop watching him so closely.

October 12

We've been on a trip to New Lexington, Ohio, with Charlie's older brother and his wife. It was on this trip that I discovered I haven't just been imagining things. It's the little things. The every day things he should be doing and either he's doing them wrong or isn't doing them at all. Now that we're back, I'm calling Dr. Stoerkel's office for an appointment.

December 18

Dr. Stoerkel called this afternoon regarding Charlie's MRI on December 11th. He said when he compared this MRI to the MRI that was taken back in March, it showed no new bleeding. I can't figure it out. If there's no new bleeding, why is Charlie getting worse?

❀❀❀

3
“The Setback”

March 29, 1993

In the last few months since the MRI, Charlie has gone down hill so fast that it’s frightening. He can’t work the microwave again, or the tape recorder he always loved. More and more he starts to talk, then can’t remember what he wanted to say.

The other day he decided to clean the coffee maker by letting it go through a cycle with a mixture of white vinegar and water and he couldn’t figure out why the mixture wasn’t coming down into the carafe. When I checked it, I found out he’d forgotten to pour the mixture into the top of the coffee maker.

These are the kinds of things he does. He calls people on the phone and starts talking to them without telling them who he is, or why he’s calling. He can’t read anymore either. He says he can read the first line, but when he tries to read the next line he has a hard time finding it. And Charlie always loved to read. He loved *Reader’s Digest*, and every day he read his Daily Devotions from the church. The *Bible* was also a must and he'd pore over it all the time. Sometimes I read to him in the mornings and at lunch, although many times it's as if he doesn't understand what I'm reading.

~

A few weeks ago, I was sick in bed with bronchitis and our twenty-one year old grandson, Grant, called from work. He said he needed a ride home because his car wouldn't start.

Charlie said he'd pick Grant up and take him home. I figured since it was early afternoon and he would only have a short drive from Mentor to Fairport Harbor and back, Charlie should be able to do it, so I said okay, and he left. When he got home, he had the strangest look on his face.

"What happened?" I asked, worried that maybe he had gotten into an accident or something.

For a minute, he just stood there leaning against the front door. Then slowly, he said, "I can't go that far from the house by myself anymore. I didn't know where I was, and I almost got lost coming home."

Two days later finally put the clincher on his driving. It was after dark and he went up to the supermarket, which is a three minute ride around the corner, to buy a loaf of bread.

When he got back home and walked into the house his eyes were filled with terror.

"I can't do it," he blurted, and I could just hear the anguish in his voice. "I didn't know where I was on the road, or where any of the other cars were on the road and I was afraid I was going to hit somebody. I don't even know how I got home."

Since that day he hasn't driven anywhere. He's afraid to, and besides, he knows I would never let him, not anymore. What's bothering me though is that I don't care where I have to drive or how much my writing is interrupted, what I care about is what's happening to us.

When other people see him they don't realize he's as bad as he is, but I'm with him every day. I see it, and I'm scared.

His personality is changing again. He's more tense, quick to anger, and rarely shows any warmth toward me anymore. I feel like I'm losing him little by little and it hurts.

Once in awhile he'll look at me and say, "I love you." however, his expression doesn't match the words. It's as if he's saying them because he thinks it's the thing to do, and in spite of the words of love, five minutes later he's back to calling me names.

He has no idea what pills he has to take or when, he can barely write his name and I know that soon I'll have to use the power of attorney.

For the past couple of days, all he wants to do is sit and listen to a cassette tape he made on Christmas day twenty years ago. He played the guitar and sang and yodeled. He used to be quite good and he's so proud of the tape that he wants to play it for everyone.

Whenever there was a holiday, he'd get out the tape recorder and we'd all sing together. He'd always interview everybody, asking the kids if they were having a good time. His kids were always so important to him.

March 30

It's 2:00 p.m. I'm trying so hard not to cry. This morning was a bad morning. We have them often now. Charlie cries and I try to console him. I hug him and kiss him and tell him how much I love him, but still he accuses me of trying to "mess up his head."

All morning it was one thing after another. He isn't going to need the lawn mower for at least another couple of months, but I just got back from taking the blade up to the lawn and garden center to be sharpened because he got the idea that he wanted it done, and he wanted it done today. Things become obsessive with him. Once he decides to do something, or he wants something done, he wants it done right then and there.

When Charlie got back from his walk with the neighbor a few minutes ago, he was crying. He told me he was sorry he was so mean to me this morning.

"I don't know why I do these nasty things," he said. "I don't mean to do them, why do I do them?"

What could I tell him? I don't know either. Our conversations used to be such fun. In fact, he was so outgoing and such a talker that he used to ask me if I didn't get tired of hearing him talk all the time. How ironic. Now I wish he could talk. I wish he could just ramble on and on like he used to. It would be so much better than this. Sometimes I get so frustrated that I feel like giving up. But I won't. I can't. I love him.

Needless to say my writing has suffered tremendously. When I'm so wrapped up in my own feelings, I have a hard time trying to concentrate on my characters and their feelings. And I get interrupted so much too. I'll be in the middle of a scene when Charlie interrupts me and then it's hard to recapture the same mood again. Yet, I think if I didn't have my books to occupy my mind I'd go crazy.

Tonight I sit here with an aching heart, wondering what's ahead for us. Today I didn't cry, but what about tomorrow?

March 31

What a day! With the pension check to cash we planned to go shopping. Even before we left the problems began. Charlie said he was going to call Carol, next door, about something. Carol's a widow who lost her husband to cancer back in November of 1992. They've lived next door for almost forty years. Carol, who is blond, taller than I am and three years younger, is more like a sister to us than a neighbor. She's helped me so much with Charlie since he's become ill. I was in the bathroom washing and I saw Charlie dial the phone, listen for a few seconds, than hang up.

"So, did you talk to Carol?" I asked while I finished washing and started to get dressed.

He frowned. "She hung up on me."

"What do you mean she hung up on you?" I straightened my slacks and pulled on my blouse. "Carol would never hang up on you," I said. "I don't think she's home. I bet you got the answering machine, didn't you?"

"No, I got Carol," he insisted, a pouting look on his face. "But she didn't wait for me to tell her who I was, and she hung up on me."

I looked out the back door, saw that her car wasn't in the garage and tried to explain to him that she wasn't home and it was Carol's voice on the answering machine. Charlie just couldn't follow my reasoning, and insisted Carol hung up on him.

~

While we were in the check out line at the store, Charlie started putting our groceries up on the counter and mixing them in with the groceries of the lady who was ahead of us.

"Don't do that, honey," I said, trying to be as tactful with him as I could be because I could see the lady was getting irritated.

He kept it up.

Finally I lowered my voice, tried to sound as forceful as I could and said, "No dear, don't do that."

I forced him to put the things back in our cart, explaining that we would put the groceries back on the counter when the counter was clear. I was flushed with embarrassment because the customers gave us a lot of nasty looks.

When we got into the car he started to fasten his seat belt wrong, and I said, “You have the wrong strap. You need the one with the buckle on it.”

“Shut up!” he yelled. “I know what I’m doing.”

But he didn’t, and all the while he was cussing and yelling because it wouldn’t fasten.

Finally I reached across him, fighting him all the way, grabbed the buckle, and said, “Here, pull this!”

He was still angry, but he took the buckle from me and within seconds had the seat belt fastened.

By the time we got home from shopping, we were both so tired we decided to take a short nap. When we got up, he couldn’t find his wallet.

“Where did you put it?” I asked, but he didn’t know.

After hunting all over the house for it, and then getting in the car and backtracking to the last store with no results, we came back home. We finally found the wallet pushed way to the back of his top dresser drawer. He hadn’t remembered putting it in the drawer.

April 1

Our grandson Braxton is almost eleven now, and Yvonne bought him a pet bird. It’s a beautiful blue and white lovebird and they named it Goomie. Charlie said he was going to call Braxton up and find out how he liked his new bird.

“What’s Jill’s telephone number?” he asked me.

“You don’t want Jill’s number. You want Yvonne’s number,” and I started to tell him Yvonne’s telephone number.

"No, I said I want Jill's number," he insisted, raising his voice this time and paying no attention to the number I was giving him.

"But Braxton is at Yvonne's house," I tried to explain. "He isn't Jill's son, he's Yvonne's son."

But he wouldn't listen. "Are you going to give me Jill's number?" he yelled. "Or are you going to keep acting like a smart ass?"

So I gave him Jill's number and he dialed the phone. Evidently Jill's nine year old son, Vincent, must have answered. Charlie asked him how he liked his bird.

Then suddenly Charlie said, "Oh, I didn't mean to call you, Vinnie. I meant to call Braxton."

After saying good-bye to Vinnie, he hung up the phone, then turned to me and said, "Boy, how dumb can you get, you gave me the wrong number. Now, what the hell is Jill's number?"

~

Things like this go on all day long, and there are times I feel like screaming. Yet, I know I have to be patient because I love Charlie and he can't help what's happening anymore than I can. But it sure isn't easy.

April 2

I talked to Dr. Stoerkel on the phone today and he wants Charlie to stop taking his Zoloft and the Diazepam. Dr. Stoerkel said the extreme confusion and mental problems Charlie is having could be caused by a toxic reaction to the medications.

Dr. Stoerkel also referred us to Dr. Geldmacher at the Foley Elder Care Center, part of University Hospitals of Cleveland. He said he felt that with Charlie's mental state deteriorating the way it is he should be under the care of a neurologist so he could be diagnosed as to just what was going wrong. So I made an appointment with Dr. Geldmacher for July 2nd.

In the meantime, I'm supposed to keep Charlie off the two medications for two weeks, then see how he's doing. I hope it works, because tonight my legs hurt so bad I can hardly stand it. All day long, we did nothing but search for his keys, his glasses and his hearing aid. And after all the shopping the other day, I think if someone yelled, "Fire!" I wouldn't even be able to budge.

April 3

We just got back from the lawn and garden center where Charlie caused a horrible scene that not only embarrassed me half to death, but reduced me to tears.

I had been up there earlier in the day to pick up the lawn mower blade we had taken to be sharpened, and while I was there, I also bought a new spark plug and filter for the lawn mower.

When I got home, Charlie tried to put the filter in the mower and discovered it was the wrong size. They had sold me one that was too big, so I told him I'd go back up and get it exchanged. He said he wanted to go with me. Fine, I didn't care. Now, I wish I had said no.

When we took the new filter back I also took the old one along with us so they could see the exact size we needed. After exchanging the filter without any problem, we left.

When we were almost to the car, Charlie suddenly stopped and said, "They gave us the wrong filter."

"No, they didn't," I said. "Look," and I held up the new filter. "It's the exact same size as the old one," and I held up the old filter too, showing him that they were exactly alike.

"But you don't understand," he said. "They threw away my good filter and gave us the wrong one."

"No, they didn't," I said. "Here are our filters," and again I held both filters up, side by side right in front of his face so he had to look right at them, but it was as if he didn't even see them.

"Those aren't our filters," he argued, and pointed to the old one. "See, that one's even dirty. They gave us someone else's filters."

"That *is* our old filter, that's why it's dirty," I said. "This *is* our new filter," and again I showed him.

Suddenly he whirled around and said, "I'm going back in there and make them give me back my filter," and he started hurrying back into the store.

I followed as close behind him as I could, but by the time I got inside he was yelling at the clerks and asking them where his filter was, telling them they'd thrown away his filter. Then he started rummaging around through all of their wastebaskets, while he continued to rant and rave and carry on something terrible.

I didn't know what to do. I tried to explain to everyone, including the customers, that he was confused and had some brain damage. By now I was in tears. He wouldn't listen to me or stop what he was doing. In fact, he didn't seem to even care that I was crying and upset. I tried to restrain him, but he was acting like a man possessed.

Finally, one of the young men behind the counter grabbed a business card, wrote his name and telephone number down on it, and held it out for Charlie to take.

"Here, Mr. Shiplett," he said. "Take this, and if the filter your wife has in her hands doesn't work, you have her give me a call and I'll come down to your house personally and give you a hand with it, how's that?"

At first Charlie looked at him rather skeptically, but then the man shoved the card into Charlie's hand.

"Here," he said. "I mean it. If it's not right I'll take care of it for you, all right?"

As soon as Charlie had the card in his hand I managed to get him calmed down enough to get him out of the store. When we got home, he went to the garage to put the filter in, and after a few minutes he came back into the house and said, "See, I told you they threw my filter away."

Since I didn't know what he was talking about, I went out to the garage to see what was wrong. There wasn't anything wrong. He was trying to put the filter in backwards. When I turned it around, the filter fell right into place and the lid fastened over it perfectly. Even though I had just proved it was the right filter, he kept insisting it wasn't.

About an hour later, he came into the house and apologized for having made me cry when we were at the lawn and garden center, and yet he didn't seem to have any idea why I'd been crying or remember anything else that had happened.

Nobody can fathom the frustration I went through at the garden center trying to get Charlie to stop what he was doing while trying to make everyone understand what was happening, when I didn't really know myself. All I knew was that Charlie was irrational and acting crazy.

April 5

This morning we went up to one of the local department stores and bought fertilizer for the lawn. All Charlie had to do was put it in the spreader and walk around the yard. By the time he was through spreading it, he was all upset because he couldn't remember where he had walked. I went out to look. I could see he had missed a great many places.

April 6

Ever since we've lived here, I've always wished I'd get called for jury duty. What an interesting experience it would be. Today I was called and I can't go. There's no way I could leave Charlie alone. Charlie was really bad all day today too. So confused and upset about everything. He woke me at 4:45 a.m., saying he knew he wasn't going to make it to heaven. He says he's so afraid God won't want him because his mind isn't good, and he can't read the *Bible* anymore.

June 18

It's been over two months since I last wrote in this journal and unfortunately things have gone from bad to worse, and I still don't have any answers.

Last night a frightening thing happened. We went to bed at 10:00 p.m. At 12:20 a.m., Charlie came into my bedroom and woke me up. "Hey, when do we go to church?" he asked.

I was half asleep yet, but I looked up at him in the darkened room and answered. "On Sunday, but we haven't been going lately."

"Well, where do we go to church?" he asked.

I sighed. "At Fairport Harbor."

"Why do we go to church?"

"To worship God."

Suddenly he stalked out of the bedroom. Since he was acting so strangely, I climbed out of bed and followed him. When we reached the kitchen, he whirled around abruptly, his eyes wide and wild looking.

"Then who am I?" he asked.

I was startled. "You're Charles Shiplett."

"Who told you I'm Charles Shiplett?"

"You've always been Charles Shiplett."

"Who named me that?"

"Your parents."

"Then who are you, and where am I?"

"I'm June, your wife, and this is our house."

"No, no," he yelled, holding his head, shaking it back and forth, and telling me he didn't know who he was.

For the next couple of hours I tried my best to get through to him, but couldn't. He just didn't know anything and said his mind was a blank.

About 2:30 a.m., I managed to get him back into bed, and he went to sleep. He woke up again about 4:30 a.m., only this time he was more rational. He knew who he was, and went back to sleep without any problems. This morning he didn't remember anything that had happened.

June 20

Last night was Saturday night and it happened again. Charlie woke up about 11:00 p.m.. He was incoherent, frightened and acted irrational. Only this time, after trying unsuccessfully to quiet him down, I gave him an extra Diazepam, and he finally settled down about 3:00 a.m..

June 21

Monday. I called Dr. Stoerkel this morning and told him what happened the past two nights. He said if it happens again to give him the Diazepam as I did on Saturday night.

June 27

Monday night it happened again. He was so frightened and had no idea what was scaring him. Luckily, for the past few nights, he hasn't had any other episodes. I hope it never happens again. It's scary for me as well as for him. I'm so afraid that one of these times he won't come out of it and will stay that way. I don't know if I could handle that.

June 28

We don't even go to church anymore. Charlie doesn't want to, which is unlike him. Attending church has always been one of the most important parts of our lives. Charlie says he can't follow the program at church. He says his eyes are bad and he needs new glasses.

I took him to the opthalmologist in May and was told there's nothing wrong with the glasses he has. It's just that his brain isn't picking up the signals right from his eyes, and there are no glasses in the world that will help.

June 29

Charlie's getting so nasty and mean. This afternoon we went to see my oldest sister who lives in a retirement community. My other two sisters live far away; one in Florida, the other in Doylestown, Ohio, so I don't get to see them very often.

Charlie hardly said two words to me all the way over to her place and it's at least a good twenty-five miles one way. On the way home, he started in on me.

"Why are you going to put me in jail?" he asked, as soon as we had pulled away from her apartment complex.

"I'm not going to put you in jail."

"Yes you are. I know what kind of a dirty bitch you are!"

"Please, Charlie, I'm not going to put you in jail. Now, sit back and be quiet."

"I want to talk."

"All right then talk," I answered, trying to keep my mind on my driving. "Only don't call me names and try to be nice.

"You won't let me. You won't let me do anything."

"What do you want to do?"

"Pipe water into the house."

I looked at him rather curiously, then glanced back to the road. "We already have water in the house," I said.

"No we don't. That just shows how stupid you are, and they're going to condemn it."

"Nobody's going to condemn our house, but if you want to put water in it, fine."

"If I do you'll put me in jail."

"I told you nobody's going to put you in jail."

"You will."

"No, I won't."

"You said you would."

"I never said any such thing."

"You're a liar, a dirty, no good liar. I heard you and I'm not going to jail just because you hate me."

"I don't hate you, Charlie, I love you."

"Well, I hate you, and I'm not going to jail either. I'll jump out of the car first," and he reached for the door handle.

"Don't be ridiculous. Keep your hands away from the door handle."

I slowed the car down. Fortunately the door handles are recessed and he has a hard time locating them.

"Please, Charlie," I begged. "Calm down. You know if you jump out of the car you'll get hurt."

"You'd like that wouldn't you, you son-of-a-bitch!"

"No, I wouldn't like it, now please, behave yourself. Just sit and be quiet until we get home, *please*."

He didn't. He kept it up all the way home. It even got worse. After driving most of the way in tears, I pulled into the driveway. He suddenly became docile and said, "I'm sorry, you're crying. Did I do something to make you cry?"

He expected me to turn off the tears right then and there. When I couldn't, he started to get nasty again, so I forced myself to quit crying, and pretend that nothing had happened.

June 30

He just doesn't do things right. If I don't stop him he wears two pair of undershorts or tries to fix the spray nozzle at the kitchen sink with a plunger. He looks right at something and says it's not there. When I ask him to do something he'll say he's doing it, when he isn't.

I just don't know what to do. I try so hard to be patient, loving and understanding, but what does a person do when all they get in return is anger and belligerence. He's like a spoiled child, but a child who doesn't know what he's doing. I have to watch him so closely. The other day it cost $39.70 to have the vacuum cleaner put back together because he decided he was going to "fix it". Only it wasn't broken.

How can I make him understand that he can't do things anymore? That his mind isn't functioning well enough to do the things he used to do.

The other day he got mad and threatened to smash me in the face. I told him if he ever does, I don't care how sick he is, I *will* call the police.

July 2

We had our first appointment with Dr. David Geldmacher today. He said he thinks he can help Charlie. He said he thinks the problems Charlie is having are caused mostly by a deep depression that set in after the first hemorrhage in January of 1992. He said Charlie hadn't been getting enough anti-depressant medication and his brain is refusing to work. I mentioned that I thought he may have had more bleeding. Dr. Geldmacher agreed that it was a possibility. He said that the bouts in the middle of the night when Charlie didn't know anything, could have been mild convulsions. He scheduled an MRI to check for bleeding and an EEG to detect abnormal brain wave dysfunction.

Dr. Geldmacher put Charlie on some medication called Midrin for headache, changed his Diazepam to Lorazepam, and ordered a new medication, called Nortriptyline for the depression. He said it would probably take at least three weeks for the medications to begin working. I don't like having to wait that long for results, but at least it's a start.

4

"The Diagnosis"

July 21, 1993

Charlie had a grand mal seizure today. It was about 7:00 a.m., and he was standing in front of the dishwasher to unload it when the seizure began and he fell right on the dishwasher door. Immediately, I called 911.

When the rescue squad and police arrived, Charlie was convulsing so badly that it took four paramedics and two police officers to strap him down to the gurney to get him into the ambulance. When they got him to the hospital, the doctors ordered a CAT scan among other tests and started giving him Dilantin to control the seizures. By 2:00 p.m., he had stabilized and it was safe to take him home.

This evening I talked with Dr. Geldmacher who told me Charlie has had more bleeding, and that he has what is called multi-infarct dementia. He explained to me that little blood vessels in Charlie's brain break and cause damage. Charlie is depressed, yes, but he also has a great deal of brain damage. The symptoms of multi-infarct dementia are similar to

Alzheimer's but multi-infarct dementia destroys the brain faster. He also said Charlie will get worse until eventually I won't be able to take care of him anymore and he'll have to go into a nursing home.

Thank God, Charlie has finally been diagnosed. At least now I know what I have to deal with, although it's not very encouraging.

July 30

The past few weeks have been like one big roller coaster ride. One moment calm and almost normal, the next like a nightmare from the *Twilight Zone*. I feel like I'm living with a madman!

August 28

We went to Charlie's niece's wedding reception today and he did pretty well. However, I did have to give him a Lorazepam to calm him while we were there because the loud music and everyone talking started to get to him.

It upsets me so much that his family sees him for a few minutes and they can't understand why I'm so concerned. He seems all right to them.

On the way home, Charlie looked over at me and asked, "What TV studio were we at?"

"We weren't at a TV studio," I answered. "We were at the wedding reception for your niece and it was at a party center."

"Oh no, we weren't," he said. "I don't know why you're always trying to lie to me. I know a TV studio when I see one. They even had an announcer there with a microphone."

"All right," I said. "If you want to think we were at a TV studio that's fine with me. I won't argue the point."

Then he said, "What am I going to do about it?"

"About what?" I asked.

"About the hose. Because when the cold weather comes our water pipes under the house are going to freeze and break."

"We don't have water pipes under the house," I said.

"I know," he answered. "We don't even have any water in the house."

Oh no, I thought, not again, but he went on.

"And since we don't have water in the house they're going to condemn it for sure."

"They're not going to condemn it," I said. "I told you that before."

"That's all you know about it. You're just dumb and stupid, that's all." He was ranting like a maniac. "I never saw anybody so ignorant."

He kept going on and on, but this time I managed to change the subject. It's so hard to contend with something like this, to keep loving someone who calls you names and treats you like an enemy.

~

I remember how nice it used to be to sit here in the evening and enjoy the TV together. And how Charlie used to laugh and joke around. I also remember how thoughtful he used to be. How warm, generous and loving, and how close we were. Now, he's so wrapped up in his own mixed up world and in his own thoughts, he hardly pays any attention to what's going on around him, or what I'm doing. He doesn't seem to have a grasp on reality, and yet, his family thinks he's just fine, that he's just a little forgetful.

Sometimes I see the old Charlie shining through, but most of the time it's like I'm living with a stranger. I've lost him and I wish I knew why. I wish I knew God's purpose for all this. Charlie seems so tormented and tonight when he went to bed, he prayed and asked God to let him die.

September 8

Charlie is having a bad day and my patience is running thin. Right now I wish he would die. I know that sounds terrible, but I have to be honest with myself and that's just how I feel. He won't listen to anything I say. He goes right on doing things when I tell him not to, and when I try to physically stop him, he tries to hit me. He starts arguments, says things, then says he never said them. So far I've always been able to stay out of his way and get him calmed down, but it scares me. This is crazy. I don't want it anymore. I don't *want* it anymore! *Oh God, please!*

~

It's 4:00 p.m. He's acting like someone who is insane.... I can't take it anymore. I wish *I* could die!

I thought life would be so nice and we could grow old together. What have I done to deserve this? I can't even have a civil conversation with him, please, God, help me.

~

It's almost 11:00 p.m. I am sitting in the living room wondering where we go from here. Today was a horror emotionally. I'm thankful he isn't bedridden. There are times I think that it would be better than this, at least he would have his mind, and I could reason with him.

I know I shouldn't feel this way, but I can't help it. We had always talked about how nice it would be when he retired and we could be together more to watch the birds and visit with our friends. Now all that's lost. I'm so glad he retired from the shop when he was only fifty-eight because at least we had seven years before this happened.

I try so hard to keep my mind occupied and keep from crying. I feel like I'm caught in a deep dark whirlpool with no way out and there's no one to help me. Sometimes I can submerge myself in my writing. For a few minutes out of the day it helps to escape my own feelings; however, it doesn't help enough because I'm always pulled back to the reality of what I have to cope with.

September 9

It's so hard to explain what he does. You have to be with him to understand. Today we went shopping. When we got home, he complained that he needed a new flashlight. He had taken the one we had apart and couldn't get it back together. I think he lost one of the pieces. I couldn't get it to go back together either.

I told him we'd go buy a brand new one, so we left for the discount store. When we got there one of the clerks directed us to the sports department where there was a whole display wall full of flashlights.

"All right," I said to Charlie. "Pick one out."

He studied all the flashlights on the wall, then said, "They don't have the kind I need."

I frowned. "What do you mean they don't have the kind you need? They've got every kind of flashlight imaginable."

"No, they don't," he said. "They don't have one that blows dirt."

I flinched. "There is no such thing," I said.

"Oh yes there is," he insisted. "And I need one."

"Charlie," I tried to get through to him, "there is no such thing as a flashlight that blows dirt."

"Oh yes there is, and I'll just prove it to you." He headed for a sales clerk who was working on one of the displays. "Excuse me," Charlie said, interrupting him, "but could you tell me where you have the flashlights that blow dirt?"

I laugh every time I think of the astonished look on the clerk's face.

"We don't have any flashlights like that, sir," he said, trying to be polite.

Charlie started arguing with the clerk about it, so I got him out of there as quickly as I could. All the way home he kept saying he didn't know why no one had ever heard of a flashlight that blows dirt.

September 10

I got away for a little while last night. Yvonne and Braxton came to stay with Charlie while I went to see Brittany play varsity volleyball at her high school. I'm so glad because after yesterday, I needed the time away.

Right now he's cleaning the closet in his bedroom. He says it's infested with spiders. It's not. I'm sure glad I'm the only one who can hear him. When the least little thing doesn't go exactly his way he starts cussing a blue streak, and the more he cusses, the less attention he's paying to what he's doing, and the worse things go for him.

~

It's lunch time. He's sitting at the table. He said he isn't going to eat because he's mad at himself for all the cussing. I'm not going to let him get to me today. I've decided that nothing he says or does is going to aggravate me. If he wants to sit there and pout, let him.

~

It's evening. He's finally settled down in bed. After his bath he came into the living room and said, "I think I'll just leave everybody."

"Me too?" I asked.

"You too," he said, and he sat on the couch. Then a few minutes later he said, "That wouldn't be a very nice thing for me to do, would it?"

"Not really."

He sighed. "Well then, I guess I'd better not."

How many times I wish I could get into his head and know what he's thinking. To other people I guess he sounds rational just saying, "Hi, how are you?" Maybe if they talked with him for about ten or fifteen minutes they'd soon understand that something's wrong.

I did very well today, but it sure is hard at times, and I wonder how long this will go on. My heart aches for what is no more, and unless someone has been through it, they just can't understand. I'm always so glad when evening comes and he goes to bed, then I can relax, watch a little television, answer letters, or read my writing magazines.

September 11

Charlie is having a real hassle with his hearing aid tonight. He seems to think it has to squeal or it's not working. He'll put it in his ear and say he can hear just fine. Then two seconds later he has it out again trying to put new batteries in because he says it isn't working. I don't know if he really can't hear with it, or if his brain isn't sorting the words out. He says he can't understand what people are saying.

"When I go to church in the morning I'm going to ask the minister why she doesn't talk through her hearing aid so I can hear her," he said.

"You mean her microphone."

"No, her hearing aid. I know what I'm talking about. If she'd just put it in her ear I'd be able to hear her."

I just didn't even bother to answer. For well over an hour he kept putting batteries in the hearing aid, then putting the hearing aid into his ear and then taking it out again, saying he couldn't hear. He was so mixed up.

I called Yvonne on the phone like I usually do. I'm always calling Yvonne, not only for moral support, but because she seems to have more insight into what's happening to Charlie than the other girls. Maybe it's because Yvonne took courses to prepare herself for a career in caring for the elderly and mentally challenged adults. She seems to have the same compassionate bedside manner as her father and she's been so helpful to us.

September 12

Did you ever get in a laughing jag when there's really nothing to laugh about? Yvonne stopped by and we got to laughing when Charlie started talking about his hearing aid again. It's tragic and ridiculously funny at the same time when Charlie says our minister at church should use her microphone so she can hear better and then he'll know what she's talking about. It's hard to keep a straight face when confronted with something like that. It's as bad as the flashlight that blows dirt.

September 13

Tonight after supper we sat in the yard at the picnic table and watched the birds and enjoyed the evening. Although the robins, redwings and hummingbirds have gone south for the winter, it was about eighty degrees out, with a warm breeze blowing off Lake Erie. Charlie enjoyed it so much.

I am so glad, too, because Charlie was upset earlier when the neighbor couldn't go for their usual walk. I wish I could go walking with Charlie but my walking days are over because of my arthritis and diabetic neuropathy, a condition that affects the nerves in my legs.

I remember years ago, how we used to walk a mile or two every evening. We never had to worry about what to talk about while we were walking either. Communication between us was always so natural. We were friends as well as lovers and we really enjoyed each other's company.

September 15

I don't know how much more I can take. He thinks he's right when he's wrong and he just won't listen. It's so hard to try to explain to people what we go through all the time, how unpredictable our lives are, how traumatic each day can be. I just hope I live long enough to see the end of it because I wouldn't want any of the children to try to cope with all of this. It wouldn't be fair to them.

~

It's 8:30 p.m. He's sitting on the sunporch and he's been crying for over an hour and I don't know what to do. I've tried everything I can think of to quiet him down, but he still just keeps right on crying. When I ask him why he's crying he says, "I don't know." It hurts to see him like this.

~

It's 9:30 p.m. and he finally went to bed. He is so tired and worn out and he says his head is hurting him. I wish things could be different.

September 17

We had a good day today. He was even laughing and joking around. It was almost like old times. His smile was there and his eyes were crinkling and full of love and mischief just like the old Charlie I've known and loved. Oh, how I wish it could always be like this.

September 18

Today everything was fine until about 2:00 p.m. when Charlie went out to wash the car. He'd been out there for quite awhile, when suddenly he came to the bedroom window and hollered, "Hey, honey, can you come out here and help me?"

"I'll be right there." I put down what I was doing and headed outside. "So, what's wrong?"

"It just won't work."

"What won't work?"

"The air hose.

I took one look at the air hose. "No wonder," I said. "You don't have the hose connected to the compressor. You've got the air hose hooked in a circle." I started to unhook the hose.

"Don't you dare touch that!" he yelled.

"But it's not connected right. You have to connect one end to the compressor and put the nozzle on the other end."

"You stupid bitch," he yelled. "It *is* connected to the compressor."

"No it's *not.* You have it in a circle. Hand me the nozzle."

"But it won't work."

"It will if you let me get them connected right." I reached down to unhook the hoses.

"I told you not to touch them!" he screamed at me. "What the hell are you trying to do, you asshole?"

"Well, you can't use it like it is, can you?"

He held the nozzle up and pressed the lever. Naturally nothing happened. "Why won't the air come out?" he yelled.

"Because it still isn't hooked up," I answered.

For a half hour I tried to make him understand. I was called every four letter word he could think of right outside where the whole neighborhood could hear. He wouldn't let me go back inside and kept insisting I had to stay and help him, yet he wouldn't let me anywhere near the air hose.

Finally I managed to outmaneuver him. I unhooked the air hose before he could stop me and fastened it up right. When I finished, I handed him the nozzle.

"Here, go ahead and turn it on," I said.

He looked dagger eyes at me, and was skeptical, but he finally turned it on. "Hey," he said. "It's all fixed."

I didn't argue with him. I was still upset over what we'd just been through, so I went back into the house.

I finished wrapping autographed copies of the books I was donating to a literary group for an auction when Charlie came in the house. He acted as if nothing had happened! I tried to tell myself that the neighbors probably hadn't heard, and it wasn't really my Charlie yelling at me and calling me those awful names.

September 19

Just as I figured, we didn't get to church today. This morning he started to tell me something but he never finished the sentence. When I gently tried to find out what it was he was trying to say, he started calling me names.

I'm not a mind reader. He says because he knows what he wants to say, that I should know too. I try to be patient, but it doesn't help.

To save being yelled at, sometimes I try to guess what he wants. Then, I get myself into more trouble because I'm usually wrong (according to him), and he gets angrier. So I wait until he stops yelling, then try to change the subject.

~

Today I got away for a few hours. This afternoon I went to the "It's Better In Mentor Days" and handed out election material for the library. Yvonne and Braxton stayed with Charlie. It gave me some time away and a chance to see and visit with friends.

It's evening. Charlie is sitting out on the sunporch. He is so mixed up and confused. All of a sudden he came in and said, "Boy, those people must think I'm crazy."

"What people?" I asked.

"Those people," he said. He pointed toward the front of the house.

I looked outside. There wasn't a soul around. "You mean the people who live across the street?"

"No, I don't mean the people across the street. I mean *those* people!" he yelled.

I just shook my head.

5

"Trying to Cope"

September 21, 1993

Miracle of miracles, we had a good day! He was happy and he went for a walk with the neighbor. He didn't buck me about anything. Even tonight. How nice if it would last.

September 22

It's Wednesday morning. What a night I had with Charlie. I went to bed at 11:00 p.m. and decided to read. While I was reading, he got up, went to the bathroom, then came into my bedroom. He was acting weird. I thought it was just because he was half asleep so I told him to go back to bed. I finished reading the chapter, shut off the light, and started to settle down for the night.

I laid there about five minutes. Suddenly he came into my room shouting, "Where am I? What is happening? What is this place?"

I turned on the light and started to talk to him. He didn't know who I was. For the next half-hour I tried to reorient him but nothing registered.

I took a chance that Carol might still be up and called next door. She came right over. He didn't recognize her either! We talked with Charlie for a half-hour or more. Then slowly, a few things started coming back to him.

Finally, we managed to get him back to bed, then Carol left. He settled down and went to sleep. When morning came, the strangest thing happened, he remembered it all and said the whole thing had frightened him terribly.

September 25

Earlier this evening Charlie was sitting at the kitchen table with all three pairs of his glasses in front of him. He kept saying that they weren't doing anything for him.

He wanted to read one of his religious books so I pointed out his reading glasses. He wouldn't put them on. Instead he just kept saying, "Look at them. They're just laying there and not doing a thing."

"That's because you have to put them on," I said. I put them on his face and pointed at the words.

While I pointed to the words, he read the words just fine. The minute I turned away, he took the glasses off, laid them back on the table and kept saying over and over, "They just don't work. I need new glasses."

I tried to change the subject, but he was obsessed with the glasses. For over an hour I tried to make him understand that he had to be wearing the glasses for them to work. It was like talking to the wall.

September 26

Yvonne came over to do her wash today. Charlie got angry at us over some trifling thing and left the house, saying he was going for a walk.

Usually when this happens he gets halfway up the street, then comes back. Tonight he didn't. When a half-hour went by, Yvonne got in her car and went looking for Charlie.

She found him sitting in the local park about a quarter of a mile from the house. He wouldn't get in the car. He said he didn't want to come back. She tried coaxing him, but it didn't work. Finally, he gave in, but insisted he'd walk home.

For the rest of the evening, he sat on the couch crying. Yvonne and I tried to console him but it didn't do any good.

Charlie's finally in bed. I can relax and proofread some of the writing I did last week. Each day keeps getting harder. I only hope I can hold out.

September 29

Our son-in-law Jim stopped by the house yesterday. I mentioned that the electrical cord was starting to fray on the light that hangs down over the kitchen table.

Jim smiled through his dark clipped beard and mustache. "I can put one in for you," he said, his hazel eyes shining behind his glasses. "I've put a lot of them in helping my brother remodel houses, and it won't cost you a thing except the price of the light."

I am so pleased about Jim's offer and so is Charlie. Charlie said he wants a light with a fan on it just like our daughter Jill and her husband Ken have in their living room. That isn't my choice, but to make Charlie happy, I'm going along with his suggestion.

October 2

Jim came over today and put the light up for us. I don't know what we'd do without him. Even though he works long hours, he always finds time to give us a hand.

The whole time Jim was working, Charlie was complaining. He kept coming up to me and saying, "Oh, God, what are we going to do? Can't you see what he's doing? He's breaking and tearing everything up. The ceiling is going to fall in."

It's a good thing Jim's easy going and understanding because this went on until the job was completed. I know what's happening to Charlie is hard on Jim. The two of them are very close and Jim is more like a son than a son-in-law.

October 3

Sunday. The family is coming over for a going away party for our grandson Grant. I can't believe he's almost twenty-two, and leaving for Florida on Tuesday.

When Jim arrived, he checked the fan to see if the blades were balanced. Charlie freaked out. He kept insisting the fan was going to fall on his head. Every time Jim turned the fan on, Charlie yelled and howled. One time he even said, "It's a monster animal. It's going to take a bite out of me!"

I don't know if the party was too much excitement for Charlie, but it took a long time for him to quiet down.

At bedtime, Charlie told me that when he's gone he wants me to ask Jim to take care of the house. I swallowed hard and told him not to worry.

October 4

Monday morning. Charlie just got up. He's standing in the kitchen looking up at the fan. "Boy, that's going to be real nice next summer when the weather gets hot, won't it?" I'm amazed. Not a word about being scared of it or anything.

~

I try to put my feelings down in this journal each day, but how do I find the right words? My feelings are so mixed up. One minute I love him, the next I hate him. I kiss him, hug him, and tell him it will be all right. My heart goes out to him, aching for the hurt he must be feeling.

Later, when I feel beaten into the ground with his persistent hostility; when he yells, swears and treats me as if he hates me, I wish I could just leave and never look at him again. Somedays I feel like I can handle it, other days I know I can't.

Most of the time I'm his mother, seldom his wife, and it hurts. He'll say, "I love you." But the warmth and intimacy we once shared is gone. I'm a widow whose husband hasn't died.

October 5

Before supper, I was out on the sunporch. Charlie came out and asked, "Where are my keys?"

"They're right there in your hands," I answered.

"Oh no, they're not." He shook his head. "These *aren't* my keys." He slammed them down on the table where I was working. "Now!" he continued to yell, "where are my keys? What did you do with them?"

"I didn't do anything with them because these *are* your keys." I picked them up off the table and held them out for him to take. He wouldn't take them. It was time for me to fix supper, so I got up, took the keys with me and set them down on the kitchen table. "Now, your keys are right here," I told him.

"I told you, those aren't my keys," he insisted.

While I fixed supper he continued to badger me by calling me names and telling me I'd better give him back his keys or else.

I went to set the table and saw the keys were gone. "Charlie, what did you do with the keys that were on the table?"

"I didn't do anything with them," he said. "Besides, those weren't my keys. You've got my keys."

I happened to glance down at his pants and realized his pants pocket was bulging. I walked up to him, reached into his pocket and pulled out the keys.

"Well, so what are these?" I asked him.

"Hey," he yelled. "Where did you get my keys?" Then suddenly his voice lowered and his brown eyes snapped angrily. "See, I told you, you had them all along."

"I did not," I answered. "I just took them out of your pocket."

He laughed sarcastically, then smirked. "You did not. See, I knew you had them. You can't fool me. I always know when you're lying."

October 8

Today we went to see Dr. Geldmacher. I always hate going because it's about a thirty mile ride and I never know how Charlie is going to act in the car.

The doctor said there isn't much more he can do for Charlie and that Charlie's behavior is expected for someone with his problems.

I asked the doctor about Charlie's hearing aid. He said it's better to just talk a little louder and pronounce the words more distinctly because Charlie's brain is unable to filter out voices and put words in order.

Charlie's next appointment is in April but Dr. Geldmacher said if at any time I have any questions, or need anything, or if anything should happen, not to hesitate to call.

After we left the doctor's office, I decided to ride out through the country since Charlie seemed to be enjoying the ride. Fall is such a beautiful time of year in Ohio, and Charlie was fascinated by all the colorful trees. It looked as if God had taken a paintbrush and just went wild with all the shades of reds and yellows. The whole while we were riding Charlie just kept staring out the window and commenting in awe about the autumn leaves. It was almost as if he had never seen fall before.

October 9

I was thinking about my conversation yesterday with the doctor. He said he wants me to try to get Charlie into a day care program at least once a week, but at thirty dollars a day, I know we can't afford it. Not right now anyway.

Unfortunately, I had to break off my relationship with the agent I had for eighteen years. Since I haven't been able to do much writing lately, and I haven't sold a novel since *Boston Renegade* in 1991, money is scarce.

I just hope it won't take too long for me to find a new agent and get back to my writing. I do need my books. Not just financially, but they help me to escape the misery I feel inside. My books are as much of an escape for me as they are for my readers.

October 13

Yvonne and Braxton stayed with Charlie tonight. Because of my writing accomplishments, the Women Business Owners of the Western Reserve nominated me, along with two other women, as a "Woman Of The Year." It was a great honor for me.

In the past Charlie would have proudly accompanied me but now he can't handle crowds or much excitement. Instead, I took Elaine, the young woman who used to be my typist. She's a dear friend and almost like a daughter to me.

We had a lovely time. Oh, to be able to talk with people and carry on a normal conversation.

While I was giving my acceptance speech, I looked toward the table where Charlie would have been sitting. At that moment, a sense of loss engulfed me. Never again will I see his eyes shining with pride or his smiling face giving me encouragement. Never again will I be able to catch the warmth of his love from across the room that always seemed to help me get through my speeches. I had a terrible time holding back the tears and there was an ache and loneliness in my heart that cut so deep it was almost unbearable.

October 15

It's 4:00 p.m. and Charlie's mad at me because I refused to let him take the car apart. For some reason, he has the idea that there's water in the gas line and he's bound and determined to fix it.

When I wouldn't let him near the car, he took off down the street. I just have to let him go because I know it wouldn't do any good to go after him. He wouldn't come back. The last time he did this he finally came back on his own, so I'll just have to wait.

He'd been gone over a half-hour. I went looking for him in the car, but couldn't find him. Maybe he went down one of the side streets.

~

It's 4:45 p.m. He's not back yet. Carol just called and I told her if I didn't hear from him by 5:30 p.m., I'd call the police.

~

At 5:10 p.m. Charlie called from the drugstore. He didn't have any money, but everyone there knows him is so they dialed the number for him. I went to pick him up.

When I got to the drugstore he started acting nasty. He wasn't going to get into the car. I pleaded to no avail. Finally, I said, "Either you get in this car, or I'm going to go back home and call the police to come get you."

He stared at me angrily for a few seconds, then reluctantly got in the car.

After supper, he apologized. He said he was scared all the while he was walking because there were a lot of dogs barking at him and he ran from two Dobermans that he was sure were going to chew him to pieces. He said, "I just barely got away."

October 16

Today is Sweetest Day. It used to mean something, now it's just another day. I tell people it doesn't matter, that it doesn't bother me, but it does. I have wonderful memories of Sweetest Day. Charlie would bring me candy or flowers along with the biggest, mushiest card he could find. I know those days are gone forever and it hurts.

October 17

It's Sunday, but we didn't go to church today. Now there really is something the matter with our car. I don't dare let Charlie know or he'll want to try to fix it. I have an appointment to drop the car off at the garage late this afternoon.

Shortly after supper, I told Charlie to get his sweater on because we had to take the car to the garage. He stared at me with the coldest look in his eyes, then said, "I thought you said there wasn't anything wrong with the car."

"Well, there is now and it's something you can't fix so please, don't give me a hard time and get your sweater on."

Yvonne and Braxton gave us a ride back home.

Charlie was sullen and quiet. I was sure he was angry. When we got back to the house he said, "Why did you tell me there was nothing wrong with the car when you knew damn well there was?"

"I told you before we left," I answered. "It's something in the electronic equipment that you know nothing about."

I thought I had gotten through to him because he didn't say anything else. Later when I went to check on him, I found him all the way up at the end of the street. Surprisingly when I went after him, he did come home with me.

After Yvonne and Braxton left, Charlie sat out on the front porch crying for most of the rest of the evening. Maureen stopped by for a visit and she tried to make him understand that we all love him, and he finally did stop crying. While she was here, she also called Jim. Jim said he'd come by tomorrow morning and help cut down the flowers that have died off, so Charlie's pleased about that.

Maureen is our other blonde, only her eyes are a warm brown just like her father's. She's a lot like Charlie and I think that's why they always seemed to clash so much when she was in her teens. Maureen grew up in the hippy era, and

I'll never forget how mortified her father and I were when our "flower child" was protesting everything.

Today, Maureen is strictly establishment. She says she always gets a big kick out of telling everyone how she almost made it to Woodstock.

How well I remember it. Right after graduation she and a girlfriend took off and were hitch hiking up to Syracuse, New York, where her girlfriend's aunt lived. A guy stopped and offered them a ride. But he said he wasn't heading their way. He said he was headed for a place up in New England where some farmer was having a concert in his cow pasture. Maureen and her girlfriend turned down the ride. Naturally, the guy was heading for Woodstock.

Maureen and Charlie's temperaments are so much alike. They're both set in their ways, a bit headstrong, sentimental, and always willing to help others. Maureen takes in every stray that comes along and she always has. I don't mean animals either. I mean people. Her door is always open even if all she has to give is a peanut butter sandwich and a floor to sleep on. She will truly give the shirt off her back even though she and Jim are struggling with today's economy.

~

One time Jim and Maureen were living on a well traveled country road and I always used to worry because she'd take in and feed every transient that went by. I told her one time, that I was worried that someday we'd get a call from the Sheriff's Department that she and her whole family had been murdered in their sleep. Her answer to me was that she just couldn't turn anyone away.

"After all," she said. "Didn't Jesus tell us that we should feed and clothe everyone, even strangers because we never know when we might be entertaining an angel unaware?" This was something her dad had taught her, so I never questioned her again.

October 18

Monday afternoon. Jim came and did a good job on the flowers even though Charlie got mad because *he* wasn't the one allowed to use the electric hedge clippers. After Jim left, Charlie wouldn't even talk to me for a while.

I hope Charlie didn't say anything nasty to Jim while there were working together. Charlie has been saying that Jim and I are accusing him of robbing and stealing things. Even if Charlie did say something though, I doubt Jim thought anything about it. I honestly think he's having a hard time accepting what's happening to Charlie because Jim keeps making remarks about Charlie getting better. I don't think Jim wants to admit that Charlie will never be the same again.

6

"Will I Survive?"

October 21, 1993

It's 11:00 a.m. The past few days have been unbearable. Charlie's been argumentative and so on edge I hated to even to talk to him. I'm hoping today will be better.

The mechanic called and said the car was ready. Carol took us up to get it this morning. Now Charlie's out raking leaves and picking up acorns. He doesn't have to. The wind is blowing so hard today its's blowing all the leaves toward the marsh at the back. There are hundreds, maybe thousands of acorns in the yard and he's down on his hands and knees gathering them one at a time and putting them in his little green bucket beside him. At least he has something to keep him occupied.

A little while ago I went into the kitchen to fix supper. There was Charlie's Dilantin on the counter. I had forgotten to give it to him earlier. When he came into the kitchen, I gave him the pill.

"What's this?" he asked.

"It's your Dilantin," I told him.

"Well, I'm not going to take it."

I frowned. "Why not?"

"Because I'm tired of being treated like a dog."

"I don't treat you like a dog. I treat you real nice and you know it. Now come on, take your Dilantin so you won't end up having a seizure like you had before."

"I don't care about any seizures," he said. "And I'm not going to take your damn pill."

"Please Charlie, you have to take your Dilantin."

"Why? Why should I do anything for you, or for anyone else for that matter? I just ought to kill the whole lot of you." He looked over at me. "Yeah, that's what I'll do, I'll just kill everyone."

"Now quit talking like that." A cold chill went through me at the look on his face. "Besides," I went on, "if you were to try to kill anyone they'd lock you up in prison and you know you wouldn't want that."

For a few seconds he just stared at me as if he was thinking over what I said.

"I didn't really mean that," he said, acting all sugary sweet. "I wouldn't really do that. Don't tell anybody I said it, please? You know I wouldn't kill anyone," and suddenly he started to cry.

October 22

Charlie started out picking up acorns today. That wasn't so bad. Now he's cleaning the gutters. The last time he cleaned the gutters Carol had to come over and put the screens back in the downspouts for him because he didn't know what to do with them.

Before Charlie came down the ladder, I asked him if he had the screens in the downspouts where they were supposed to be.

"No," he said.

I asked him three more times because I'm so used to him telling me the wrong thing that I wanted to make sure. Each time I asked him if the screens were in the downspouts where the belonged, he said "No."

Even though my arthritis makes it nearly impossible for me to climb up and down stairs, I climbed up the ladder to take a look. "Hey, the screen's in here," I yelled to him.

"Yeah, I know." he yelled.

"But it *is* here." "Yeah, I know it's not," he answered.

How long can my patience hold out? It's madness.

Tonight was the Cleveland Author's Recognition Banquet. Elaine went with me and we really had a good time, although I think I made a fool of myself. There were ten people at a table, and I was enjoying talking to them, answering their questions and discussing my fiction writing. Suddenly I realized that everyone else was through eating their salad and mine was still on my plate.

When I realized I had been monopolizing the whole conversation, I apologized to everyone and started to cry over my embarrassment. Elaine told them what I was going through and while she was doing that, I managed to pull myself together.

~

Every day I live with a man I can't talk to normally. We never really have any conversations, and here I was with people who could talk with me, people I could relate to, people who were able to interact with what I was saying. I felt like I was in heaven.

I got home about midnight. Charlie was in bed. Yvonne and Braxton had stayed with him and Yvonne was worried that Charlie might have lost his bottom teeth. I had warned her that he gets mixed up taking them out at bedtime and she said she'd help him. She said Charlie went into the bathroom and took them out himself when she wasn't looking. He had his top teeth in the tooth cup, and he wouldn't tell her where his bottom teeth were. He wouldn't open his mouth for her to see if they were still in there either, and she couldn't tell by just looking at him. I told her not to worry, they were probably in his mouth.

October 23

Sure enough, when Charlie got up this morning, his bottom teeth were in his mouth. Before leaving last night I had promised Charlie I'd take him anyplace he wanted to go today. He chose to go see one of his sisters and her family.

On the way to his sisters, I said to Charlie, "I'm going to stop by the mall and pick up our lottery tickets, okay?"

"Sure," he said. "And I'll even go in with you."

I was lucky, and I found a parking place right next to the entrance.

"Now, you're sure you want to go in with me?" I asked.

He nodded. "Oh yeah."

"Okay," I said, and I unbuckled my seat belt.

However, Charlie didn't move, he was just sitting there as quiet as could be.

"I thought you were going to go in with me," I said.

"I am," he answered, and yet he still just sat there.

I got out of the car, leaned back in one more time and said, "Are you coming?"

"I *am*!" This time he acted irritated.

I closed the door and walked around to the back of the car. After standing there for a few seconds, I realized he wasn't budging. I just shrugged then went in to buy the tickets.

When I got back out, I got in the car, looked over at him and said, "I thought you were going to go in with me."

He looked right at me. "I did!" he said just as if I had said something stupid. I just shook my head and started the car. I guess in his mind he did go in with me.

~

It still irritates me that most of his family does not accept how bad he is. I was hoping the visit today would give them some insight into what's happening. I doubt that it did.

They sat there and talked about things they did when they were kids. He remembered some of them. When they asked him how he was doing, he knew enough to say, "Fine." Mostly he sat and listened. I knew by some of the things they said that they don't believe me when I tell them he's in another world. I know he's pretending to listen, but they seem to think that he really *is* listening. If he had to repeat anything, he couldn't. But they never ask him to repeat anything, and they never ask him any questions.

~

There was one funny incident today though. I was in the kitchen with Charlie's sister and her daughter telling them Charlie can't follow the story on television anymore. His sister said, "Well look, Charlie's sitting on the couch in the living room and Dad (meaning her husband), is talking to him and Charlie seems to be listening just fine."

I nearly laughed out loud when her daughter said, "Oh, Mom, you can't tell anything by that. Let's face it, Dad can sit and talk to the wall and make it look like the wall's listening to him." I think her daughter believed me, but I don't think Charlie's sister did. Every time I tell his sister how he acts she always says, "Oh, that happens to me all the time. I'm always doing things like that." I told her if that's the case, she'd better get herself to a good neurologist because there may be something wrong. But she acted like she didn't hear me.

October 24

Charlie was gathering up acorns. The wind was blowing and the temperature was somewhere in the high sixties, so I decided to hang the sheets I was washing out to dry.

While I was hanging the sheets, I saw Charlie go into the garage. I didn't see him come out again, so I figured he must have come out when I wasn't looking. As I started for the house, I heard funny noises coming from the garage. Curious to see what was going on, and worried that Charlie might be in some sort of trouble, I walked over and opened the garage door. There was Charlie, just standing there holding the garage door key in his hand. His eyes were as big as saucers.

"Boy, am I glad to see you," he said, relief in his voice. "I was stuck in here and couldn't get out. There's no keyhole."

And he was right. There is no key hole on the inside. It's locked just by turning a small knob. The keyhole is on the outside.

"But the knob isn't turned, the door isn't locked," I told him. "All you had to do was turn the doorknob and the door would have opened."

"But there was no hole for the key," he went on.

I tried to explain to him that he didn't need a key. "All you had to do was turn the doorknob. And besides that, even if the door was locked, you could have hit the button for the garage door opener and you could have gotten out that way."

Charlie didn't understand. For the next few minutes he just kept telling me how relieved he was that I found him.

~

I went back into the house and decided I'd make him an applesauce spice cake while I watched the football game. Charlie has always loved applesauce spice cake, and now that his allergies don't seem to bother him anymore, he did enjoy it.

~

Now he's at the kitchen table crying. He's insisting he's going to hell. I wish he would quit thinking like that.

October 25

Today we went to Parkman, Ohio, to see Charlie's brother and his wife. All in all it was a pretty good day. But then, it usually is when we go visiting because I don't have to watch him closely and for some reason he controls his animosity around others.

The problem with visiting is that most of our friends and relatives live quite a distance from us and Charlie's so unpredictable on long trips. Every time we get into the car, I pray that the trip will be a good one.

October 26

It was about 3:30 p.m. when I saw Charlie heading for the lawnmower with his socket set. Before I could get outside he had the filter off and was trying to get it back on, but couldn't.

That's something I've learned to do through all this. I can take off lawnmower blades to be sharpened, remove filters for cleaning, and I can even fill the mower with gas and oil.

With the filter back in place, Charlie said he wanted to clean up the lawnmower.

"Fine," I said. "Only you'll have to bring it over to the garage by the man-door so we can reach it with the air hose."

Well, he brought it over to the garage all right, then proceeded to take the filter off again.

"Why did you do that?" I asked him. "We can't blow dirt off the mower without the air filter. The dirt will get in the motor.

"It will not," he said.

"Yes it will" I argued, and I took the filter out of his hand. "Now, let me put the filter back on."

"No!" he shouted, and slapped it out of my hand.

When I tried to pick it off the ground, he headed for the air hose.

"Oh no, you don't." I snatched the nozzle off the end of the air hose as quickly as I could, then ran into the garage and hid it. I can't afford to have him ruin a good lawnmower and have to pay some two hundred dollars for a new one. But that did it.

"I'm going to smash your face in," he shrieked at me. "I'll be glad when you're dead and gone and I don't have to look at your ugly face anymore. I wish you'd just disappear. I hate the sight of you."

He was so upset that I ran next door and got Carol. Between the two of us, we managed to quiet him down and clean the lawnmower, but not before he took a swipe at me with the screwdriver.

~

This isn't my Charlie. More and more I realize that my Charlie died a long time ago. The man I'm living with now is saying and doing things that my Charlie would never say or do. But I'll stick by him and I'd like to think that if things were reversed, he'd stick by me too.

People ask me, "How do you stand it?" I don't really know, but I do know that I have no choice. I can't afford to pay someone to come in and take care of Charlie, and he's not physically sick to warrant a nursing home, so there's nothing left for me. I must stay here and do the best I can.

October 27

About 2:30 p.m., Charlie started in again about his keys. They were right in front of him on the table but he kept asking me what I had done with his keys, demanding that I get them for him. The more I told him I didn't have them, that they were on the table in front of him, the madder he got. All the while, he was poking and pushing at me with his clenched fist.

Finally, I called Yvonne and told her what was going on. She tried to convince him that what I was telling him was true but he didn't believe her either.

Maybe I should have gone along with him and said I had the keys but I tried that once before and he demanded I produce them. When I couldn't, he got even madder, so I wasn't about to try that again.

~

It's 9:00 p.m. and he's been acting weird all evening. He went into the bathroom, got his pajamas on, then came into the living room and asked, "When is the woman across the street coming over?"

"She isn't," I answered.

"Well, I hope when she does come she has some hope for us," he said.

I have no idea what he's talking about and I don't think he does either.

Now he's asking, "Why didn't we do what we were going to do after church with those bottles?"

I haven't the faintest notion what he means. "With what bottles?" I asked him.

"You know what bottles. The bottles at the church."

"There are no bottles at the church."

"Yes, there are," he answered.

I'm writing this while he's talking to me and he has no idea I'm even doing it. Besides, he just doesn't seem to care what I'm doing anymore except when he thinks I'm hiding his keys or something equally ridiculous.

October 31

It's Halloween. Unlike those days when our daughters were little, Charlie didn't pay any attention to the kids when they came for handouts tonight. To him, it was just another day. I remember how excited they used to get when Halloween came around. Charlie always got excited, too. He was a great father and seemed to have as much fun on Halloween as the kids.

I would always carve the jack-o'-lantern and he would take the kids trick or treating. Charlie would dress up as an old scarecrow or ghost so the kids wouldn't catch on to the real reason he went along, to keep them safe. The kids loved it, and sometimes they'd even help paint his face.

After the girls got too old for trick or treating, he would always try to make the neighborhood kids have fun. Charlie always got a big kick out of making things scary for them.

November 1

Today was a very bad day for me. I ate some leftover Halloween candy and I think my sugar is up because my legs have been hurting me so much that I can hardly stand the pain. Unfortunately it hasn't helped my disposition much and I haven't meant to be, but I guess I've been a bit of a crab. To make matters worse, Charlie didn't make it to the bathroom and had an accident in his pants.

Charlie had to take a bath in the middle of the day because he got so messy. He used to be able to sit down in the tub without any problem at all, but today, he had a terrible time.

When I made him sit down to make sure he was cleaned and rinsed good, he sat down so awkwardly he almost fell. I don't know if it's his coordination, or if he just didn't know how to sit down but I'll never make him sit in the tub anymore if I can help it. I was afraid he was going to get hurt.

I hope to God it was just a one time thing. I don't know what I'll do if he starts messing his pants all the time. I know people with Alzheimer's usually end up with lack of bowel and bladder control, but I've been hoping that since Charlie has multi-infarct dementia, that he won't.

~

Every day I feel as if I'm playing charades. Charades is a game, and it's fun to play at parties, but when you're playing it twenty-four hours a day, it can really get to you. Like the day he came up to me and wanted to know if we were going to the field.

"What field?" I asked.

"You know, the field."

"Honey," I said, "I have no idea what you're talking about. What field, where?"

"The field, the field," he repeated. "The field where the soap is."

"What soap?"

He grabbed my hand. I got up from the chair where I was sitting as he dragged me into the bathroom.

"The soap, the soap," he said, and he pointed to the bar of soap on the bathtub. Then he led me into the utility room and pointed to the can of laundry detergent. "You know, the field with the soap."

Suddenly it dawned on me.

"You mean the discount store with the open field next to it?" I asked him.

"Yeah, the field where the soap is," he said, relief in his voice.

I know it must be terribly frightening for him trying to search for words that just won't come out, and I feel so sorry for him.

Now he's tucked in for the night. If I didn't have a little quiet time like this at night I think I'd really be in trouble. For just awhile I can sit here, watch TV and pretend that nothing's wrong, and my life is just as normal as it used to be. I know I'm only kidding myself, but once in awhile it doesn't hurt.

November 2

It's 7:30 p.m. I think Charlie has really flipped out. He keeps saying it's too hot in here even though the thermostat is set on seventy and I think it's cool.

He's started cursing and swearing and yelling and saying it's so hot he can't breathe. Although he's in his pajamas already, he got his jacket on and has gone outside, saying he'll find a place where he can breathe.

I finally got him back in the house, but I honestly don't know what I'm going to do with him if he acts like this when the weather gets bad.

November 3

I just lost it. All day long he's been ignoring me. He hasn't said one word. You'd think I didn't exist. Finally, I got so angry I yelled at him and told him I hated him, and right now I do. Right now I'd like to walk up to him and start pounding on him and just keep pounding and pounding, then he'd know I'm here.

The books I've read say to distance yourself. After forty-three years of marriage, I don't know *how* to distance myself.

I don't believe it. I just don't believe it. Suddenly he looked over at me as if he were oblivious to anything I had said and calmly asked, "Are you upset about something?"

"You're damn right I'm upset!" I yelled. "And you'd be too. I'm sick and tired of all this. You're treating me as if you hate me. Calling me names and refusing to talk to me."

I just wish I could leave and never have to see him again. Not *this* man. There's no way out. I hate him! I hate the things he does. I hate what's happening to my life and what's happening to him.

I'm sorry. I take that back. It feels good to let it out, but then I'm ashamed for telling him just what I think because I know he doesn't understand.

November 4

It's Thursday, and I hope I never have to see another day like today. Today I realized why my legs have been aching so much more now than they used to. I have to follow him around all day to keep checking on him. There are so many things. He leaves lights on in rooms, opens drawers and doesn't close them, uses things and doesn't put them back, and he doesn't know how to put his clothes on a hanger.

He can't even put a new roll of toilet paper on the roller without getting all mixed up. The last time he tried, I had no idea what he did with the roller and I had to buy a new one.

He'll call me to see a speck of something on the floor, or just to ask me some dumb question that doesn't even have an answer. It's no wonder my legs feel like I've been running a marathon race.

I don't mind helping him with the essential things, like bathing, or brushing his teeth, or washing his hair, but it really gets to me when he hollers, "Come here!" I go to see what he wants and he has no idea why he called me, or what he wanted.

7
"I'm Not Cut Out For This"

November 5, 1993

Yvonne happened to stop by this afternoon. After talking for a few minutes, we decided we should go outside to check on Charlie. Am I glad we did! He had taken a couple of extension cords out of the garage, plugged one in the electrical outlet on the side of the house, and had stretched them to the back of the lot.

"What are you going to do with them?" I asked him.

"I'm going to use the weed whip on the leaves."

"But you can't mulch leaves with a weed whip," I told him. "Besides, the doctor said you're not supposed to use the weed whip because you could get hurt."

"Then I'm going to use the leaf blower," he said, quickly changing his mind.

Fine, he can't get hurt using a leaf blower. Or can he? I watched what he was doing. He tried to hook up the extension cords, but one of the cords had a ground on it and the other didn't. Charlie couldn't figure out why he couldn't plug them together.

Yvonne and I tried to tell him it would work if he reversed the extension cords. We even tried to show him how to connect them, but Charlie wouldn't listen. He told us we were doing it wrong and marched next door to get Carol.

However, to his dismay, Carol agreed that we were doing it right and helped us hook it up. By now he was furious. When we tried to show him that now he could blow the leaves to the back of the lot and down over the hill, he flew into a rage. He pulled the lawnmower out of the tool shed and started it.

"Now what are you going to do with that?" I asked him.

"I'm going to show you," he yelled, and his eyes were wild, the cords in his neck standing out like ropes. "I'm going to do whatever I want," and he headed right for the extension cords that were still plugged in. He was going to run over them with the lawnmower.

Yvonne grabbed him by one arm, I grabbed the other and we tried to hold him back to keep him from running over the cords.

"Please, Charlie, stop it!" I screamed at him. "You're going to get electrocuted if you do that!"

Well, he paid absolutely no attention to either of us and kept straining, trying to break our hold and get away from us. While we wrestled with Charlie and the lawnmower, Carol ran toward the house and unplugged the cord.

From then on it was downhill with him all the way. The more we tried to appease Charlie and be nice to him and calm him down, the more irrational he became and he wouldn't listen to any of us. Charlie even told our neighbor on the other side of us that his yard wasn't his yard. Charlie said it was our yard. Thankfully, the neighbor knows what's going on.

Charlie was so stubborn and ornery that Carol told me I'd better call the doctor to see if there wasn't something he could prescribe for Charlie to slow him down, or one of these times one of us was going to get hurt, and it would probably be me.

Carol and Yvonne stayed outside, trying to talk some sense into Charlie, while I went into the house to call Dr. Geldmacher. However, the doctor was on his way to Florida and it took awhile for his office to reach him on his car phone. He said he would order a new medication called Haloperidol that should help.

I went back outside to see if Yvonne would go to the drugstore and pick up the prescription. Charlie was climbing a ladder to clean leaves out of the gutters; however, Carol and Yvonne seemed really upset and pulled me aside where Charlie couldn't hear us.

Carol said that while I was on the phone with the doctor, Charlie gave them quite a scare. They were at the back of the lot near the hill that goes down into the marsh trying to reason with him, only Charlie was acting completely irrational. "My God, you should have seen him," Carol said, "You know that ramp that Charlie built in the back yard so he could push his wheelbarrow out and dump leaves into the marsh? Well, Charlie ran out onto the ramp, yelled to Yvonne and me that he could do whatever he wanted and nobody could stop him, then grabbed an old wild grapevine that was hanging from one of the trees, and swung on it, out over the marsh!"

"We thought the vine was going to break," Yvonne added. "And we were screaming at the top of our lungs telling him to hang on."

Carol shook her head. "I don't know what kept him from falling. I never saw anything like it in my life. How Charlie ever managed to hang on until the vine brought him back to the hill, I'll never know," Carol said. "He must lead a charmed life."

I'm so glad Carol knows what's going on. It really helps. As soon as they were both calmed down, Carol helped me put all the cords and tools back in the garage while Yvonne went to the drugstore and got the new medicine.

I gave Charlie one of the pills while he was still out working in the yard. Later, when he came in the house, he went right to his bedroom and went to sleep. I didn't say anything to him, but just let him sleep. He slept for about two hours and when he woke up he was in a better mood.

About 9:00 p.m., he suddenly remembered he had swung out over the marsh on the vine and became upset.

"I don't know how I could have done such a dumb stupid thing like that," he said, and he insisted on calling both Yvonne and Carol and apologizing for having scared them.

It seems strange that sometimes he can remember things he does, other times he doesn't.

November 6

When I talked to Dr. Geldmacher's secretary on the phone yesterday, she told me that the doctor wants me to be sure to find a support group. I called the Alzheimer's Association and I think I've found one nearby, only I can't get in touch with the group leader until Monday. Maybe if I go to their meetings, I'll be able to find out how other people are coping with this. I sure hope so.

November 7

After having such a hard time with Charlie the past few days, I prayed as hard as I could and asked God to let the Holy

Spirit help me. I asked Him to show me how to cope, and then I remembered what the books I was reading kept telling me, "distance yourself." So that's what I'm trying to do.

Really, my way of distancing myself is just a way of playing make believe. I tell myself that the man I'm looking at isn't Charlie. That Charlie's gone and the man who's here with me is just someone who's sick and no longer in control of what he's doing.

When I get him into bed, I tell myself that nothing is wrong. Charlie just went to bed early like he used to when he was working. Everything is all right, and our world isn't topsy turvy. I tell myself that I don't really need to be loved anymore, that love isn't a prerequisite for existing.

Sometimes I cry, sometimes I just want to scream because pretending doesn't always work, and sometimes I just want to die because the distance isn't always there. I can't change my situation, I can't understand it, I'm just stuck with the way things are. So I gulp back the tears, tighten my fists and tell myself there will be an end to it someday.

November 11

Charlie has been acting like a lost little boy. He's even more confused the past few days. Sometimes I hate myself for getting upset with him.

Charlie used to be able to put the dishes in the dishwasher. He'd do a good job, too, but now he puts small items on the bottom rack instead of the top rack, and places things in the way of the spray arm. Instead of throwing the coffee grounds into the garbage the other day, he dumped them into the dishwasher. It took me over half an hour to clean up the mess. He used to be able to wash windows with no problem. Now he seems to think he has to take the windows all apart to wash them. I also caught him trying to vacuum the lint from the dryer filter without having the hose connected to the vacuum cleaner.

~

After Charlie went to bed last night, I sat by the fireplace watching television. Instead of going to sleep, he kept getting up and going back and forth between the sunporch and his bed. Each time he looked worried and was mumbling to himself. I asked him what was the matter. He acted confused. After questioning him a little more, I managed to find out what was going on.

Yvonne had brought him some children's picture books from the library. One of the books was about big monster trucks. There was a picture of a monster truck on the front cover and the truck had the biggest tires I'd ever seen. Charlie had been looking through the book prior to going to bed. When he finished reading the book, he set all three pairs of his glasses down beside the book. Somehow he thought the monster truck on the book cover was going to drive over his glasses and crush them.

I realized he was serious about it to the point of crying, so I went out onto the sunporch with him, turned the book over, and brought his glasses into the kitchen.

"Thank God," he said, his voice filled with relief. "I thought they were going to be crushed. Oh thank you, thank you so much."

I gave him a warm hug and a kiss and he went back to bed. How do I accept something like this? I accept it with tears in my eyes, pain in my heart, and a lump in my throat.

November 12

Charlie was smiling when he woke up, and breakfast was almost like old times. In fact, everything was going along well until after lunch when we had a go around about his keys.

During supper, he gave me another problem even more frustrating. He would ask me something and when I'd give him the right answer, he would say it was wrong. He challenged every answer I gave him. If I tried to ignore his questions, he'd threaten to hit me.

After dinner he followed me into the living room and continued to challenge everything I said. I couldn't believe what was happening. I started to cry but my crying had no effect on him.

I felt like I wanted to die because there was no escaping him. He wouldn't shut up or leave me alone. My arms began to ache. My chest felt like I'd been hit by a truck. I couldn't hold back the sobs and yet he kept on relentlessly. I didn't know what to do. I felt like I wanted to kill him because my whole world was being turned upside down and the mess was landing on me.

I've heard prisoners of war talk about being brainwashed and now I think I can understand how they feel. The badgering, the fear, the horror of not knowing how to respond. It's the most frustrating, emotionally draining experience a person can go through.

~

It's 10:45 p.m. and he's finally asleep. I honestly don't know if I can ever go through another night like tonight. There's no way to prepare for this. I sit here in the aftermath trying to sort out and understand how something like this can happen, and I wonder if anybody could benefit from knowing about my experiences.

November 15

Tonight I went to my first support group meeting. I was nervous and didn't know what to expect. I didn't know if I should talk about Charlie, or what I should say, because this was an Alzheimer's meeting and Charlie has multi-infarct dementia. I wasn't sure what kind of help I could get, but I was going to find out.

I arrived a little early and was surprised to find how friendly everybody was. They came up to me and said, "Hi, welcome. We're glad you're here." During the meeting they asked me who I was caring for, and I found myself telling them everything. They really understood and I came home feeling like I had new friends.

November 25

Thanksgiving. We had a quiet day with just Yvonne and Braxton here for dinner. Nothing like the boisterous Thanksgivings we used to have when all the kids were home.

Charlie was irritable and cranky all day. He has no concept of time and was impatient about everything. Tonight he didn't take a bath, but just washed, then he came to where I was sitting in the living room and asked me where his pajama bottoms were. When I told him he was wearing them, he suddenly began to cry.

November 30

Last night about midnight he came in to my bedroom, woke me up, and wanted to know why he wasn't in bed. He then asked me how he could get back to his bedroom. For the next few hours he kept coming into my bedroom, I'd walk him back to his bedroom, tuck him in, only to have him show up in my bedroom again.

By the time the wee hours of the morning rolled around I was so weary that I didn't know what to do, so I prayed. God is the one who has given me strength through this whole thing. Whenever I get to the point where I don't think I can make it, I've asked God to let the Holy Spirit take over my life and help me whatever way He can, and I've always seemed to get through another day. I know our problems are a long way from being over, and I continue to pray all the time that God will keep me strong because I know I can't do it on my own.

December 5

It's the first Sunday in December. Christmas will be here soon. I have such mixed emotions about the holiday season this year.

Jim has promised to get the artificial Christmas tree out of the attic for us. The last time Charlie tried to get something out of the attic it was almost a disaster. There's only a partial floor, and I was so afraid he was going to fall through the ceiling.

We did get to church today, only for the first time in my life I felt alone there. Not because God wasn't with me. I know He was there. I could feel the Holy Spirit comforting my heart, and even though everyone there is my friend, I felt a sense of being all by myself, just God and me.

I guess it's because no matter how much church members would like to comfort me, and I'm thankful for all their concern, there's no way they can share what I'm going through. Only those who have been through something like this can know the pain and helplessness that drains me each day. The anger I fight knowing there's no way to change what's happening. There are a few who have had spouses with dementia, and they do know. But the rest? They couldn't imagine in their wildest dreams what it's like to carry this in my heart.

It's *my* heart that's being torn in two as I watch the man I love die a little at a time, and yet Charlie's not dead—not physically anyway. I can still hold his hand and put my arms around him, but I can't talk to him the way I did before. I can't share my world and my life with him anymore because he's no longer in my world. Not really. He's in a world that's all mixed up and there's no way out for him either.

December 8

Christmas is two and a half weeks away and I still haven't decided what to do about the tree. Charlie has been saying he doesn't want it up (which is so unlike him), but I just love seeing the tree lit up, shimmering and colorful. It brings back so many memories.

When the girls were little, we'd always wait until about two days before Christmas to get our tree. We'd bundle up in our warmest clothes, and if the weather wasn't too bad, Charlie would drive us out into the country to a Christmas tree farm. There we'd climb into a huge sleigh pulled by Belgian horses and with sleighbells echoing in the snowy air, we rode out to where the evergreen trees grew.

What a time the kids had deciding which tree they wanted! Usually they'd want one that wouldn't even fit in the house. Charlie was always patient and enjoyed picking out the right tree as much as the kids did.

After we cut the tree down, we'd have a snowball fight while waiting for the sleigh to return and take us back to the barn where hot chocolate was waiting for us. After helping Charlie tie the tree onto the roof of the car (because it rarely ever fit in the trunk), we'd usually sing Christmas carols most of the way home.

How long ago that was. And yet those Christmases seem like yesterday.

December 10

About 9:30 p.m., Charlie came out of his bedroom and said, "You've got to call somebody, get somebody and do something or the house is going to burn down."

"Now, wait a minute," I said. "What are you talking about? The house isn't going to burn down."

"Oh yes, it is," he insisted. "It's going to explode. There's gas and electric in the garage and if it isn't shut off, there's going to be a big explosion and everything's going to burn," and he headed for the main switch box to start throwing the breakers.

I had a terrible time keeping him away from the switch box. Every time he opened it, I'd reach out and slam it shut. He was getting hard to handle and physically threatening.

I finally got him away from the switch box, but he kept insisting that he had to go out to the garage and take care of the gas. "We don't have gas! We have electric for everything," I reminded him.

"The electric will make the gas blow up and everything will be burned," he said.

I grabbed the portable phone, called Yvonne and asked her to talk to him. After a few minutes, I could see she was getting nowhere so I asked her to hang up and I called Carol.

She came right over, talked to Charlie, and then both of us followed him out to the garage.

It was a cold, rainy, miserable night, but Charlie was convinced, the garage was wired wrong and everything was going to explode.

Then Carol got an idea. She told Charlie to plug in his compressor. At first he wasn't going to do it, but then he gave in. After the compressor had been plugged in for a few minutes, she said, "Okay, now unplug it Charlie."

I didn't think he was going to, but then he suddenly reached over and unplugged it.

"See," she said. "Now it's going to be all right. You got it unplugged and it isn't going to explode after all. Now isn't that great?"

Charlie was so pleased that when he got back into the house, he said he could go back to sleep and not be afraid anymore. What a transformation!

8

"Making It Through The Holidays"

December 13, 1993

The Christmas tree is finally out of the attic. I decorated it all myself. I think Charlie hung one ornament. I love to turn out all the other lights in the house, leaving only the tree lights on to watch them sparkle. The house looks festive with the tree and a couple of poinsettias—one in front of the fireplace, and the other on the coffee table.

Tonight was our seven year old granddaughter, Erica's, Christmas program at school. I dropped Charlie off at Yvonne's because he didn't want to go. Besides, it would have been too much for him to sit through. I thank God that our daughters and their children realize how sick Charlie is and that they understand when I can't always make it to their school activities.

Tonight's program started at 7:30 p.m. and it was 9 p.m. when I picked Charlie up at Yvonne's. By the time we got home, he was so tired that he went right to bed without taking his usual bath.

December 19

Last night Charlie said he wanted to go to church. I set the alarm for 7:30 a.m. but he woke me up at 6:30 a.m. saying it was time to get up or we'd be late.

I told him it was way too early and sent him back to bed. He stayed there about forty minutes, then came back in and woke me up. This time I gave up. I figured for twenty more minutes it wasn't worth the hassle.

I was starting to fix breakfast when he asked, "Why did you wake me up so early? You woke me up way before it was even light out."

"I didn't wake you up. You woke me up," I answered.

"You liar, you. You know damn well you're the one who woke me up. Why are you always lying to me like this?"

Not wanting to argue with him, I didn't say anything. For the rest of the morning, he kept calling me a liar. No matter what I said, he accused me of lying. He even called me a stupid bitch and said God was going to get even with me for all my lying.

I tried to smooth things over and just ignore what he was saying. Ordinarily, I would never attempt to go to church when he is in this kind of a mood, but I felt that if I didn't get a chance to talk to others, I'd go crazy.

All the way to church, he kept saying it was the last time he was ever going to go to church with me and he continued calling me a liar. Even when we got there he was still angry and belligerent, that is until we got inside.

The minute we entered the church, he suddenly became as nice as he could be. You'd think he had never said an angry or unkind word to me in his life. He was just like Dr. Jekyll and Mr. Hyde. I was shocked, yet relieved, and hoped the rest of the day would be better. Unfortunately, it was only the calm before the storm.

We got home about 1:00 p.m., and had lunch. Then out of the blue, he said, "I have to go fix the faucet in the utility room."

"There's nothing wrong with the faucet in the utility room," I said.

"Oh yes there is. It makes a horrible noise and it needs a new washer."

I knew what he meant. The only time the faucet ever made noise was when it wasn't turned on all the way.

"You're lying again." he said. "It's broken and you know it."

In order to appease Charlie, I told him I'd call Jim and ask him to put in a new washer. Since Jim wasn't home when I called, Charlie agreed to wait until Monday when I could call again.

Not even five minutes later, Charlie was back in the utility room looking for his wrenches. Again, I tried to convince him that the faucet wasn't broken. This time he wanted me to call his nephew who lives right around the corner from us. I tried to make him understand that it was Sunday and his nephew was always busy on Sundays. Charlie insisted, so I dialed the number, then handed him the phone.

His sister must have answered the phone, and said his nephew wasn't home. Charlie tried to talk to her, but he must have had her all mixed up because nothing he was saying made any sense. He finally hung up.

Charlie was determined to take the plumbing apart, so I called my old standby, Carol. Her son, Roy, came over with her. Roy is tall, dark, and built like a wrestler. If need be, he could handle Charlie. When they found out what was going on, Roy fixed the faucet.

They were on their way out of the utility room when Charlie said, "Hey, he broke the faucet! Now the hot water's coming out of the cold water faucet and the cold water's coming out of the hot water faucet."

"They are not," I said. "Now look," and I turned each of them on and showed him that they were both all right.

Charlie kept insisting that Roy had reversed the faucets and headed for his butane torch, saying he was going to unsolder all the water pipes in the utility room.

It took two hours for the three of us to convince him nothing was wrong, then Carol and Roy left. A few minutes later, Charlie started again, only this time, I managed to get to the utility room first.

"You're not going in there," I said. "There's no way I'm going to let you take the plumbing apart and then I'll have to call a plumber."

"Get out of my way!" he yelled.

The next thing I knew he had hold of my shoulders. He was shoving me backward ahead of him into the utility room. I yelled for him to stop, instead, he started hitting me back and forth on the head and shoulders with his open hand. Then he slammed me up against the furnace on one side, and the laundry tubs on the other. When we got next to the laundry tubs, he quickly grabbed my hand, and held it as tight as he could.

"Now I'll prove to you that cold water is coming out of the hot water faucet," he yelled, and started to pull my hand over to hold it under the faucet.

I panicked. He had turned on the faucet. The water coming out was so scalding hot it was steaming. I don't know where I got the strength, maybe it was because I was so petrified, but I managed to break his hold on my wrist. A couple of times he tried to grab my hand again, only I was able to twist around to keep out of his reach. Then he pushed me against the closet at the end of the utility room.

"Now," he yelled. "You're going to stay right there until I get these pipes fixed," and he reached for his tool caddy that was on one of the shelves.

All the while I kept begging him to stop, to let me out, talking to him through my tears and then finally I said, "I just want to go back into the living room and watch the football game."

For some reason, he immediately put the tool caddy back, and started to leave the utility room. I was right behind him. As he was headed out of the room, he was saying he'd do whatever he wanted to do and no one was going to stop him, not me or anybody else.

When we reached the bathroom, instead of staying behind him, I opened the door that goes into the vestibule, unlocked the back door and ducked outside; then I ran as fast as I could over to Carol's. I didn't ring the doorbell, but just opened the door and ran inside. By now, I was crying hysterically, and after telling Carol and Roy what had happened, they came back to the house with me. We couldn't calm Charlie down. Instead he grabbed his coat and hat and took off walking.

While he was gone, I called Dr. Geldmacher and he told me that when Charlie got back I should give him a Haloperidol pill, and then to give him another pill at two hour intervals until I had given him four. He said by that time Charlie should be calm enough to handle.

When Charlie got back he still wouldn't listen to me or do anything I asked him to do. Carol came over again, and between the two of us, we tricked him into taking the Haloperidol.

It took almost an hour before Charlie calmed down enough for Carol to go home. She said she was afraid to leave me alone with him. While we talked to him during that hour, he told us he wanted to die. He said that he had gone over to his sister's house, and then ran all the way home. He said he ran right out in the middle of the road hoping the cars would hit him.

~

It's 11:30 p.m. He's finally in bed. The doctor said if anything like this ever happens again, I'm to do the same thing with the Haloperidol. The doctor also said if Charlie should ever hit me again, or I feel like my life might be in danger, not to hesitate to call 911.

I hope it never happens. But who knows, I never thought it would come to this. In all the years we've been together, Charlie has never hit me or even threatened me. Even if we did have an argument, he'd always go for a ride until he cooled down. I know it's the disease, but it's still scary.

December 23

Today it is cold and snowy out, but Charlie and the neighbor took their walk anyway. I try to encourage him to keep walking as long as the neighbor is willing because I know it's good for him.

I know Charlie will never be "just fine" again. Each day I try to figure out what I can do to make things better for him and try to get him interested in something. This morning, I tried to get him to color in a coloring book I bought for Christmas, but it was too tedious for him.

He's found a religious book that seems to keep him happy. It's about a man who was visited by angels. Charlie says he's reading the book but he seems to be on the same page. It keeps him happy though and that is fine with me.

Tomorrow is our traditional family Christmas get-together. The girls will come home with their families and we will exchange presents, have a potluck lunch, and sing Christmas carols.

Charlie always looked forward to our get-togethers before he became ill, and he said he's looking forward to seeing everybody tomorrow. I worry because sometimes all the confusion can set him off like it did at Grant's going away party. I hope everything will turn out all right and that Charlie will enjoy the day.

December 24

It's Christmas Eve and the family get-together turned out better than expected. Charlie even joined in the fun when we called Laura and Tom and Grant in Florida and wished them all a Merry Christmas.

There were times throughout the day when Charlie was confused, and I think he was relieved once everyone finally left and the house was quiet, but all in all, he seemed to weather the pandemonium quite well.

January 1, 1994

It's half past midnight. The last two years have brought so much pain and sorrow that I'm afraid to wonder what 1994 will bring. Whatever it is, dear God, please give me the strength to accept it. I'm not very good at things like this. I have a tendency to crumble in the face of adversity. I can't help it, it's just me but I believe that with Your help, I will get through this.

The house is quiet now. I watched the New Year come in on television. Charlie got up shortly before midnight and was sitting at the kitchen table eating some sherbet when the big ball dropped in Times Square. I gave him a kiss and wished him a Happy New Year, but by his response, I knew he didn't grasp what was going on.

The tree will come down next week and if Charlie is alive next Christmas, we won't put up a tree. I think all the fuss and confusion of the holiday scares him.

January 9

Charlie has been docile, like a confused child the last few days. For the first time in months, he put his arms around me and gave me a hug. It felt so good. Oh, he's said he loves me, but he hasn't shown any affection. Anyway, for just a few minutes, it seemed like I had my old Charlie back.

There are times I love him so much and feel so sorry for him that it hurts. Other times, I wish it would just end somehow but I guess these feelings are normal.

It's late and I'm exhausted. It's nice though, sitting here when it's quiet and knowing I don't have to jump and run to find out what Charlie's doing. I can't let what's happening to Charlie conquer me. And with God's help, I won't.

January 10

Am I really two weeks into the new year? It seems like time is going so fast, yet each day drags by. I guess it's because I'm so alone most of the time. The tears come too often now, and the pain. The emotional pain that gnaws inside me like a cancer, destroying all the happiness that once was. All I ask is that I won't fail. But why me? Oh, God in heaven, why me?

January 11

One nice thing about all the snow this year is that it keeps Charlie busy. He shovels our snow, Carol's snow, and even goes across the street to shovel the neighbor's snow.

If there was just something *else* he could do to amuse himself it wouldn't be so bad, but there isn't. He can't read, he can't draw, he can't understand much of what he sees on television (although he does seem to like the rodeos and fishing programs), but I don't know. When he tries to listen to music on his walkman, or even the radio, he says it sounds all jumbled up to him and he can't enjoy it.

I have tried to find things that will occupy his time, but so far, nothing seems to work except snow shoveling and walking. I guess because neither activity takes any rational thinking.

I went to my support group meeting tonight while Yvonne and Braxton stayed with Charlie. It is always nice to get away for a while. I have a writing commitment on Thursday so I'll be gone again. I hope he'll be as good on Thursday as he was tonight.

January 12

Every day I feel like I'm on an emotional roller coaster, a merry-go-round that's running backwards. People used to tell me my eyes sparkled. That they were always alive and filled with warmth and love. Now I know there's only sadness there because the sadness is in my heart like nothing I've ever felt before.

~

It's 9:45 p.m. He's in bed and I think he's finally fallen asleep. Earlier, he was trying to convince me that he has three sets of teeth and he was looking for the third plate. I have no idea what kind of third plate he thought he had.

I don't know if he's having more infarcts or what, but it's so hard to handle him when he's like this. How do you convince a man he's looking for something that doesn't exist?

~

The support group meetings do help. Members say not to cross the person. I try to apply this technique to what goes on every day. I try not to cross Charlie as long as what he's saying or doing isn't important. Who cares if he wants to think a truck on a book can run over his glasses, or the ceiling fan is a monster. By not crossing Charlie and agreeing with him when he says things that don't make sense, neither of us gets frustrated.

January 23

I used to say we had good days and bad days. Now I say we have good minutes and bad minutes because he has such unpredictable mood swings. Yet, I hate myself because I feel so trapped and I shouldn't feel like this. I should be selfless and glad I'm here to help him.

I try to make life as comfortable for him as I can. But I can't help the anger, hurt and frustration that fills me. I ask for strength. Where is it? Am I that bad a person?

I'm thankful he can still dress himself and brush his teeth, most of the time, but even these are becoming a challenge for him.

Last night he said he wanted to soak his teeth in peroxide before brushing them. Good and fine. But he kept filling his tooth cup with peroxide, coming and asking me what to do, then pouring the peroxide out. This went on for almost an hour until I finally took care of everything myself. Even then it took me about half an hour more to convince him his teeth were clean enough to put in his mouth.

These are the things that try my soul. The little things no one else ever sees. The things that strain my own sanity. There are times when things almost seem normal, then within minutes we're playing charades again.

He will ask me the same question ten times or more and each time I'll answer him. He'll also ask me to repeat things because he says he can't hear, but if I raise my voice and talk real slow to make sure he hears, he'll yell. Then he'll call me names and tell me to quit shouting at him.

If I ask him to repeat something I may not have heard, he gets furious. He'll ask me to read to him and I will. However, while I'm reading, he'll interrupt me and start talking about other things, or he'll get up and walk off. If I even try to stop reading, he'll get all upset and yell at me.

When we get ready to go somewhere he can really try my patience. He doesn't understand that I can't get both of us ready at the same time.

Yvonne said she'll come and stay with him if I want to get away for a few hours. But where would I go? Whenever I go out he wants to go with me. When I go to my support group meetings, I lie and tell him I am going to a library meeting. Charlie knows I've been associated with the library for a long time as a friend and trustee, so he doesn't question my going. Otherwise, I don't know if I'd get out of the house without an argument.

Meanwhile I'm trying to work on my books and it isn't easy to be creative when my life is in such turmoil. When I write I put myself into my character's situations. I close my eyes and see each scene before I write it, and there are days now when I can't do it. The feelings just won't come. I always have one ear tuned in to what Charlie is doing, and where Charlie is and I can't concentrate. When the scene begins to develop, and I think I've finally captured my idea, Charlie usually interrupts me and my train of thought is gone.

It's so easy for people to say, "Hang in there, remember, God's with you," then they get to go back to a normal world. Where's my normal world?

Charlie's in bed now and it's so peaceful. It's times like this when I feel guilty for even complaining. At least I have these moments to myself. I try to unwind, but it's so hard. I usually end up just sitting in the chair by the fireplace, sometimes watching TV, sometimes working on a scene I tried to write earlier in the day and couldn't, but most of the time I just gaze about the living room and wonder where our lives are going. What happens next?

January 24

Monday afternoon. Ever since we got home from shopping, it's as if someone short circuited him. The stores were very crowded but I thought he seemed to be handling it okay. Maybe going shopping was too stimulating.

I don't know what's going on in his head, but very little that comes out of his mouth is rational. The worst part is that he says he's right and tells me *I'm insane*.

When he looks at something, says it's broken and I say it's not, he says, "You're having hallucinations."

Late this afternoon, he said he was starved and began pestering me to hurry and fix supper. He said he couldn't wait to eat but when supper was on the table, he suddenly got up and went outside. When he came in to eat about half an hour later, he got mad because the food was cold.

Tonight Braxton was here doing some of his homework on my computer. In one way, I'm glad he knows how his grandfather is, but sometimes I wish he could have only the old grandpa to remember. The grandpa who used to do all those fun things with him, like wrestle around and shoot the BB gun. Every time Braxton would do something Charlie usually did, Braxton would always say, "Hey, that's another way we're alike, Pa."

Braxton has said it hurts him to see his grandfather like this, but he never stops saying, "I love you, Pa."

January 28

It's 10:00 p.m. and Charlie's in bed. I feel so trapped and it's getting worse every day. Nothing I say or do is right. If I could just have a normal conversation with him once in awhile it wouldn't be so bad.

I was talking with Yvonne on the phone. When I hung up Charlie said, "Why did you ask Yvonne about the lottery tickets?"

"Because I asked her to pick them up for us since I'm not planning to go out tomorrow."

Suddenly, he got the meanest look on his face. "You know, you're ugly," he said, and his eyes narrowed nastily. "What an ugly thing to do. Why don't you ever let me buy the lottery tickets? You probably keep all the money for yourself."

"I don't win any money, "I answered. "And even if I did it would be our money, not my money."

As usual he didn't listen. He just kept ranting and raving about how nasty and ugly I was.

~

At bedtime, I took a can of peaches from the refrigerator. "How would you like a nice cold dish of peaches before going to bed, Charlie?"

"Why? You'll probably just hand them out to all the neighbors."

~

There are times when I hate myself because I know Charlie is sick, but my pain is so deep and I can't find peace.

There was a time yesterday when I just wanted to hit him and hit him and keep on hitting him. Then tonight, his comments made me so angry, I wanted to throw the can of peaches at him. Sometimes I'm afraid I'll crack and maybe I won't be able to stop myself and that scares me.

Doctors and nurses leave their patients at the hospital, visitors go home. I have no place to go. There are a couple of women in my support group who took care of their husbands before they went into nursing homes, then passed away. These women still come to meetings to see if they can help others. I asked them how they survived.

After listening to them, I don't think they really know *how* they made it through. They took one day at a time, tried to stay as focused as they could, and shared their plight with others whenever possible, grabbing onto every new suggestion they thought would help. So that's what I'm trying to do.

I'm also praying for strength because I've learned that there are some caregivers who haven't survived. They've died of heart attacks, had nervous breakdowns, and became physically incapacitated. I realize that unless I take care of myself, I might not survive either. Then who will look after Charlie?

9

"The New Year Is Starting Out Badly"

January 31, 1994

Charlie was in so many different moods today. There were frustrating times, then other times when he actually laughed and kidded around, just like old times.

The other day Yvonne compared living with Charlie like living with someone who has multiple personalities. She said there's no way to know from one minute to the next which one will appear.

I think it's a perfect description. Sometimes he's the stubborn little boy, pouting and refusing to talk and doing nasty little things as if to get back at me. Other times he's the grown up Charlie who thinks he can do anything. And sometimes he's the docile, contrite Charlie who thinks he's a terrible person and apologizes for everything. Then he's the soft-hearted Charlie who would do anything for anybody and would never think of calling me names. I never know what to expect. Today, I guess he's mostly the confused little boy, so I hugged him a lot and I tried to make him smile as much as I could. I think it helped us both because today I don't feel like crying all the time.

~

Earlier, I asked him to take an empty Limburger cheese jar out to the recycling bin for rubbish collection tomorrow. In a way, it was actually funny, and I chuckled about what he did, because for some reason he was having an awful time and didn't want anyone to see him taking the jar out. I certainly don't know what's wrong with eating Limburger cheese, but when I finally convinced him to put the jar in the recycling bin, he ended up hiding it in the bottom of the bin. Then he came back in the house and said, "Boy, I sure hope nobody saw me."

February 1

Something really weird happened this evening. Charlie was sitting on the couch watching television, and suddenly he looked over at me and asked, "Didn't you tell me one day that we were married?"

I was a little surprised, but glad he remembered something. "We've been married forty-four years," I answered.

He looked astounded." I don't believe it," he said. "Are you sure?"

"Yes, I'm sure."

He frowned. "We couldn't have been married that long."

"Well, we have been."

Then he started looking around the living room. "Where are the kids?" he asked. "This isn't the house on Ward Drive. What happened to the house we live in?"

"This is the house we live in now," I said. "But the kids don't live here anymore, they're grown up. Maureen's married to Jim and they live in Fairport Harbor with Brittany,

Jill and Ken have Erica and Vinnie and live in Eastlake, Yvonne and her son Braxton, live in Willoughby. Laura and Tom live in Florida, and so does Maureen's son Grant".

"Oh no." He shook his head in disbelief. "They can't be grown up, I don't believe this." Then he started remembering things from back in the late fifties and sixties.

He remembered the house we had lived in before we moved here, the trailer park where we lived when we first got married, and the real estate dealer who had sold us this house. He remembered that when we first moved into this house he had to pick up old cans and bottles from all over the back yard because it was nothing but a field. He even remembered the cars we owned back then.

He said his head was reeling with all the memories and that they were rolling in so fast he could hardly keep up with them. It was weird because everything he was remembering was from when our kids were little.

By bedtime I had to give him some extra Lorazepam to calm him down. Even at that, he didn't go to bed until 11:00 p.m. It was such a strange thing to have happen, and it was also a little frightening.

February 3

I've had some pain on my left side for about a week now and I'm glad I went to the doctor today. He said he's quite sure it's diverticulitis, an inflammation of the large intestine. He prescribed some antibiotics and put me on a liquid diet for a week. He said if I don't show any improvement, then he'll have to put me in the hospital and run some tests.

If I have to go into the hospital, Yvonne has promised that she will have Charlie stay with her. I know she'd take good care of him, yet I'd hate for her to be responsible for

Charlie because sometimes he can be so hard to handle. I just hope and pray the diet and antibiotics work.

February 6

This year is really starting out on the wrong foot. For the first time in over forty years, I managed to make a lulu of a mistake and mess up my checking account. Then the fuel lines on the furnace froze, and today, another car smashed into ours! Nobody was hurt, but I just hope this isn't a taste of what the rest of the year's going to be like. I have enough trouble just taking care of Charlie.

February 8

I just had to write tonight because today was such a good day. Not only because I got away for a while when I went to the junior high school and gave a talk to some of the students about writing, but also Charlie was in such a good mood most of the day. Oh, we had a couple of minor altercations that I managed to handle pretty well, but mostly, he seemed a lot happier than usual. Something I rarely see in him anymore—happiness. His eyes were even crinkling when he laughed, just like they used to. When I kissed him at bedtime, he smiled, and I saw the old Charlie, the Charlie I've loved all these years.

February 10

I'm exhausted. We went to the claims adjuster today and it's going to cost almost $2,500 to have the car fixed. Of course Charlie doesn't realize what's going on except that the car looks terrible and he keeps crying and saying it will never be pretty again. We made arrangements with the garage and will drop the car off Sunday night.

February 12

I took a real good look at Charlie today. It seems like a terrible thing to say, but as each day goes by, I'm remembering less and less of what he used to be like. I don't know if this is a normal reaction or not. I try to visualize him talking and laughing, being his old self, but all I can see is the bewildered, sometimes angry, sometimes sad, man he is today.

February 13

About 3:00 p.m., Charlie came in from outside and I said to him, "Keep your things on because we're going to be leaving right away to take the car to the garage. Yvonne's here and she's going to drive us back." I was putting on my coat.

Charlie said, "Okay, I know," but then proceeded to take off his things.

"No, Charlie," I said. "Keep your coat and things on."

He paid absolutely no attention to me. He had his boots off and had hung his coat and hat up in the vestibule.

When he came into the kitchen and saw that I had my coat on he said, "Where are you going?"

"I told you," I said. "We're taking the car to the garage."

"Well, why didn't you tell me," he said.

"I did tell you," I answered.

"You did not. See, there you go lying again. Well, just for that you're going to have to wait now until I get my things back on."

When we finally got in the car, I noticed I didn't have my sunglasses with me. The sun was out, making the glare from the snow really bright, so I headed for the house to get them.

"You wait here, I'll get them," Charlie said.

I was skeptical, but he insisted he knew right where they were, so I waited. I waited and waited. I finally turned off the motor and went in to see what he was doing.

Unfortunately, Charlie had an accident in his pants and he was in the bathroom. After I got him washed up and had put a clean pair of undershorts on him, he started to put on his boots. I kept telling him he had to put his pants on first, but he just kept telling me to shut up, that he knew what he was doing. He was also trying to put both boots on the same foot. When I tried to stop him and show him what he should do, he started yelling and cussing.

Yvonne, who had been patiently waiting in her car, came into the house to see what was going on. She said, "Why don't you just let him go, Mom. When he walks outside and freezes his rear end off he'll be glad to put on his pants."

"You know you're right," I said. I chuckled as I left him in the bathroom and told him to go ahead and do it his way.

Pretty soon he called for me to help him get his pants on, and we were finally able to leave for the garage, but I never did get my sunglasses!

February 17

Today was one of those days you hope never to see again. Charlie insisted the dryer was broken. He kept saying the drum wasn't going around fast enough and it was going to catch fire.

I spent the entire day trying to keep him from getting his screwdrivers and taking the dryer apart.

I screamed, pleaded, begged, threw a tantrum, gave him some Haloperidol like the doctor said, and finally, I threatened him.

"If you don't listen to me," I said. "I'm going to have to call the police and have them put you away where you won't be able to take anything apart. Do you understand that? Do you know what that means?"

If I survive this winter it won't be Charlie's fault. I know I don't want to see another day like today.

February 19

I don't know where to turn anymore. Charlie's determined to take the dryer apart and my threats don't phase him.

Before he went for his tools, though, he said, "I want you to call Yvonne up and tell her to come down here right away because you're crazy."

"I will not call her and tell her that!"

"Well, you'd better," he yelled. "Because if you don't I'm going to hit you," and he shook his fist at me.

So I dialed Yvonne's number. I got her on the phone and handed the receiver to him. He said, "I don't know why your mother called you, Yvonne. I never told her to call you. Besides, she keeps telling me the dryer needs fixing, when it doesn't."

Yvonne knew right away something was wrong, and since Jim had taken Braxton somewhere for the day, she was able to come right over.

When Yvonne arrived, Charlie continued to pretend I was the culprit. “I don’t know why your mother keeps insisting the dryer’s broken,” he told her. However, within minutes, he switched back to what he’d been doing before she came.

We knew we were in trouble when he headed for his tool caddy. I went to the utility room and stood directly in front of the dryer. I was in tears at the thought of having to pay for a new dryer.

Charlie came over to the dryer with his tools. I showed him how well the dryer worked, but he paid no attention to me. When he saw that I was standing with my arms over the dryer, practically laying on it so he couldn’t get near it, he said he’d go get Roy, and that Roy would show us the dryer was broken. I hoped Roy would be able to calm Charlie down.

“Fine,” I said. “I’ll send Yvonne next door to get him.”

Roy came over and looked at the dryer. “Charlie,” he said, “There’s nothing wrong with your dryer.”

“I know,” Charlie said. “That’s what I’ve been trying to tell June, but she insists it’s broken.” Roy and I exchanged surreptitious glances seconds later when Charlie added, “Now, you see, all I have to do is take the front of the dryer off, take the drum out, and I can show you what’s wrong.”

“But, Charlie, it’s *not* broken,” Roy repeated, and he took Charlie’s arm. “Come on, I’ll take you over to our house and show you that ours works the same way.”

I guess it didn’t do much good because the minute Charlie got back home, he was all set to take the dryer apart again.

I ended up giving him extra medication, and Yvonne and I spent the rest of the evening trying to keep him away from the dryer. It was just horrendous.

~

It's 11:40 p.m. He's been in and out of bed at least five times already. The doctor said the medication is supposed to make him groggy, but it hasn't, not yet anyway.

Right now I'm so angry and upset. All I do is cry. I want to be able to lead a normal life, but there is no such thing for me. Not anymore.

February 20

Sunday. Charlie was in to wake me at 7:00 a.m., I didn't feel like arguing with him so I got up. I was so tired though and my eyes were burning and swollen from all the crying I did last night.

After breakfast, Charlie said, "Let's stop at Maureen's after church. I want to see if Jim will come over and help me fix that dryer."

It was the last straw. "I'm not stopping at Maureen's and you're not going to do anything about that dryer," I yelled. "And I don't want you to even mention the dryer anymore, do you understand?"

"But I've got to talk to Jim in order to get it fixed."

"The dryer's not broken," I continued, yelling at him. "And I am not going to stop by Maureen and Jim's after church."

"You have to," he said. "How am I going to be able to ask Jim what to do?"

"Shut up!" I just couldn't stand it anymore. "I don't want to hear another word about that dryer."

But he didn't shut up. He kept it up all the way to church and by the time we got there I was so upset. I tried to keep from crying, but it just didn't work. I cried through the whole service. Silently, yes, but the tears just wouldn't stay inside. Fortunately everyone at church understands.

Charlie didn't even notice I was crying and paid absolutely no attention to me. After the service was over, we got in the car and headed for home. He looked over at me and asked, "Well, are we going to stop by Maureen and Jim's?"

"No!" I yelled, but all the way home he kept at it, just like he had done on the way to church, insisting that if something wasn't done with the dryer it would catch on fire and burn the whole house down.

After we got home he headed for his tools again, but this time I had the cordless phone in my hand.

"You take down one tool, just one, and start heading for that dryer and I'm calling 911," I warned him. "You're not going to take that dryer apart and that's all there is to it."

He stared at me for a second with dark hostile eyes. Then slowly, reluctantly, he pushed the tool caddy back farther on the shelf where it had been sitting. He came out of the utility room and headed for the front of the house.

I breathed a sigh of relief. I just know that one of these days I'll really have to dial 911. I'm trying so hard to pull myself out of this. To distance myself so I can handle it, but I'm a human being, not superwoman.

~

Every time I try to find a book written by someone who has a relative with Alzheimer's or any type of dementia, I can't. I'm hoping that if I can read about someone who has gone through what I am going through, I won't feel quite so alone. So far, the books I've read have been written by people who have others helping them, or they have money to hire people to come in and take care of their relative so they can come and go as they please.

~

It's so easy for people who have never been through something like this to give advice. They tell me to just put it in God's hands, or just ignore him. The people at the support group say to distance myself and I try that. But there are times I just can't distance myself no matter how hard I try because Charlie is relentless and obsessive when he gets something into his head.

~

I know God has helped me through this so far, and I pray He won't desert me now, but I feel so lonely and trapped.

~

I don't mind tying Charlie's shoes, or combing his hair and helping him get dressed, or consoling him when he cries. And I can put up with some of his nonsense like the times when I put a nice meal on the table and he lets it get cold, or even when he tries to put his shoes on the wrong feet.

But I can't handle it when he does destructive things and when he won't listen to reason. I also have a hard time handling the verbal abuse, and physical threats. I'm scared so much of the time.

February 21

I feel a little better tonight. I talked to Dr. Geldmacher this afternoon. He told me I could use the Haloperidol at my discretion, just so Charlie didn't have more than four pills in an eight hour period. He also told me not to hesitate to call him for help. When I told him that practically everything Charlie says is irrational, he said it's to be expected, because Charlie's brain is so badly damaged.

February 22

One minute I hate Charlie, the next I feel sorry for him, the next I remember what he used to be like and I can't help loving him.

If waiting on him hand and foot would make him well, I'd do it. But spending every walking moment of every day with someone who's not in touch with reality is like slowly sinking in quicksand.

February 23

Today's the second day I gave Charlie some extra medication and it seems to be helping. When I combed his hair this morning, he was playing peek-a-boo with me and giggling like a little kid. I hugged him a lot today because for the first time in a long time, I really felt like it.

Before Charlie and the neighbor went for their usual walk, I helped him get his coat on, then gave him some extra quarters for coffee at the drive-in. Charlie smiled at me and said, "Gee, I like it when you get me ready like this, it's fun."

10

"Things Are Getting Worse"

March 2, 1994

How on earth did I make it this far? March is supposed to be the harbinger of spring. I hope so. I'm looking forward to seeing the crocuses against the snow, the trees starting to bud, and the daffodils pushing their way up through the wet soggy ground toward the sun and a new life.

Charlie has been getting much worse. I tried to get away with not giving him extra medication today. I guess I feel guilty about using medication to control him.

After supper, Charlie wanted to take out the rubbish. I was watching a television show and didn't want to miss the ending, so I tried to stall him. Then, during the commercial, rather than taking the time to tell him what to do, I just grabbed the wastebasket, took it out and emptied it myself.

Unfortunately, Charlie followed me, and saw what I was doing. He flew into a rage, unhooked the rubbish can lids and kicked the cans filled with rubbish and garbage all over the yard. When I tried to clean up the yard, he said he'd hit me, so I threatened to call 911.

He finally calmed down, but not before taking his medication. I guess I'll just have to keep on using the Haloperidol four times a day so I can manage him. Even though he's still mixed up and confused, it does keep the violence down to a minimum, and that's what scares me, the violence.

~

If he becomes too violent then I can't keep him here anymore, and just the thought of not having him with me hurts terribly. In spite of everything, I love him.

He went to bed about 8:30 p.m., but then got up several times before settling down for good. The last time he came out of the bedroom, he walked over, stared at the TV and said, "Is that for real?"

"No," I answered. "It's a movie. It's make believe."

He shook his head. "Well, is this room real?" he asked, and he looked all around the living room.

"Oh yes, the living room's real."

He frowned. "That's weird."

"You look tired," I told him, and he did. His eyes were all bloodshot. "Why don't you go climb in bed and get some sleep?"

He sighed. "I don't know how, how do people sleep?"

"They just lay down, shut their eyes and stay like that until they finally fall asleep."

"You're kidding."

"No," I went on. "That's the way we all go to sleep."

"I don't believe it," he said, and he was very serious. "If that's what you want me to do, I'll try," and he went back into the bedroom.

~

I've asked God to forgive me if my taking out the rubbish, so I could finish watching a television show was selfish. Sometimes I just can't help wanting to be me and wanting to be a normal person. If I'm to survive this, I have to have an outlet for my own thoughts. I have to be able to enjoy some of the things I like to do, or I'm afraid I'll crack under the strain. I can't isolate myself from everyone except Charlie and what he wants and demands. If I do my life is over, too, and I don't want that to happen. All I ask is the strength and courage to go on, *please*....

March 6

We were going to church this morning. We even got up on time. I was eating my breakfast, but Charlie had already finished his. He started putting his dishes in the dishwasher and wanted me to get up and help him. When I continued eating, he started throwing everything into the dishwasher any old which way.

He'd lift a fork and holler, "There, how do you like that?" and he'd throw it in, then repeat the same thing with all the rest of the dishes.

Naturally, I had to leave my breakfast at the table in order to stop him. I put the dishes in right so nothing would get broken; however, as soon as I'd go back and start eating again, he'd open the dishwasher, remove the dishes, and throw them back in again.

For some reason the Haloperidol doesn't seem to be working today. I don't know how much longer I can handle him. I try not to provoke him, but with Charlie I don't have to do anything except be there to provoke him.

I loved the Charlie he used to be, but I have to admit to myself that there are times I hate this Charlie. A person can be verbally abused just so much before it kills any love that was there. I know it's the disease and not him, but tell that to my heart.

Yvonne has told me she's frightened for me, but understands why I'm trying to keep him here as long as I can.

One thing that bothers me though, is what this is doing to me. I don't even feel like a person anymore. I feel like a nothing. I'm losing my identity and feel as if the world doesn't know I exist At least people in prison know that it was their own doing that got them where they are. I have no control over what's happening to me, to us, and it hurts to see our lives destroyed.

I see other people growing old together and enjoying each other's company and I wonder why my life can't be like that? What did either Charlie or I do that we have to be forced to go through this nightmare? All we ever wanted to do is what's right, to please God.

March 7

After supper, Charlie and I went to Yvonne's to pick up Braxton. When we arrived, Charlie went in to use the bathroom. He was only in there for a few minutes when Yvonne came to the door of the building. "You might as well go park the car in the parking lot," she said. "Dad's had an accident and he's going to need you."

He needed me all right! And the most irritating part about it, was while I was cleaning up a horrible mess, Charlie was laughing. For some reason, he seemed to think it was funny!

March 14

Tonight Yvonne and Braxton stayed with Charlie while I went to my support group meeting. Many people don't know that the Alzheimer's support groups are not just for Alzhemier's caregivers, but for friends and relatives of those with Alzheimer's and related cases of dementia. The meetings help me immensely.

After Yvonne left, Charlie said he wanted to go to bed. Fine. I gave him his medication, got his ice water for him, tucked him in bed and thought, oh good, now I'll get to watch television.

Ten minutes after I tucked Charlie into bed he was back out in the living room pestering me and telling me the program I was watching was dumb and stupid.

Finally, at 11:00 p.m. I thought maybe if I go to bed, he'll go to bed. I had just started to doze off, when I heard him come into my room.

"Where's my bed?" he asked me. "I can't find my bed."

"You were in it," I answered.

"Oh no, I wasn't," he said. "And I can't find it."

I walked him back to his bedroom, tucked him in bed, gave him a kiss, and told him, "Now you stay there."

Ten minutes later he was back in my room again asking me where his bed was. Again, I took him back to his bed, and again he came back into my room, "Where is my bed?" he said. "I don't have a bed to sleep in!"

This went on until 1:30 a.m. I must have taken him back to his bed and tucked him in at least twenty times. Each time I'd think he was going to stay put and I'd start to doze off, he'd be back in my room.

About 1:45 a.m., my patience gave out. Instead of taking him back to his bed, I turned on the lights in the kitchen, told him I was hungry, and started frying some mushrooms and green peppers for a sandwich.

All the while I was at the stove he sat on the edge of the sofa watching me, then when I had the sandwich made, I cut it in half.

"Would you like some?" I asked.

"Sure," he said, and he came to the table.

After we finished eating I looked over at him. "Well, do you think you can go back to bed and stay there now?" I asked him.

He seemed congenial enough. "Sure," he answered.

So I tucked him back in bed again, gave him a kiss, told him I loved him, turned off the lights, except the night lights, and went back to my own bed. Ten minutes later, he was back in my bedroom.

"Where's my bed?" he asked, just as bewildered as he'd been the first time he had asked me. "I can't find my bed."

"All right, if you won't let me sleep," I said. "I might as well do something useful."

By then my adrenaline was pumping and I probably couldn't have slept if I'd tried. So I got up again, turned the lights on in my office, and at 2:15 a.m., I sat down to work at the computer.

For a few minutes Charlie stood at the door to my office and just stared at me, "What am I supposed to do?"

"You know, I don't really care what you do," I said. "You can go to bed, sit up, or just walk around the house, whatever you feel like doing because I have work to do. How's that?"

He watched me a few minutes longer, then went into the living room and sat on the couch. The lights in the living room were off, but he didn't seem to mind.

After sitting there for about fifteen minutes, he got up and went into his bedroom. I peeked out of my office just in time to see him climbing into bed.

Good, I thought, but he's not going to do this to me again so I continued working for another half hour. Then at 2:45 a.m., I went in and checked on him. Thankfully, he had finally fallen asleep. I quickly shut off the computer and climbed into bed, but it was at least a half hour longer before I could relax enough to drop off to sleep. I kept expecting him to come in any minute.

March 15

Today he didn't remember anything that had happened last night, and he was so hard to handle all day. I feel sorry for him and yet I'm so frustrated with what's going on in our lives. Sometimes the anger rages inside me. It hurts knowing that things will never get any better.

March 18

Another Friday has rolled around. I was supposed to go away tonight, but by the way Charlie was acting, I was afraid to leave him with Yvonne and Braxton. Am I glad I didn't!

He got up out of bed about 10:30 p.m., went into the bathroom, then stopped by the kitchen sink. I was in the living room sitting by the fireplace, but I knew where he was.

"While you're at the sink will you bring me a small glass of cold water?" I asked him.

Instead of bringing me the glass of water I wanted, he went into his bedroom, got the thermos of ice water that he keeps on his bedside stand and brought that over to me.

"I don't really want your thermos full of water," I explained to him. "All I want is a small glass of water."

"Okay," he said, and he took his thermos back into the bedroom, then went into the kitchen.

Well, I thought he was going to be bring my drink of water any minute. Instead, I heard loud, weird noises coming from the kitchen. Jumping up from my chair, I hurried into the dinette area just in time to see Charlie raise his arm and throw a handful of ice cubes into one of my cooking pans.

Charlie had taken all of my pots and pans out of the cupboard, lined them up on the kitchen counter, had all the empty ice cube trays strewn around the counter, and was throwing water and ice cubes into all of the pans. Water and ice cubes were everywhere.

"What are you doing?" I yelled.

"I have to," he shouted. "We're running out of water."

"We aren't running out of water," I yelled back. "Now, put everything down and leave it alone."

"Get away!" he threatened and he took a swing at me.

I ducked out of his way, then tried to get by him to grab some paper towels and wipe up the mess.

"No!" he shouted. "Get away," and he swung at me again, then pushed me toward the kitchen table. "If I don't get more water in these pans, we're going to be out of water by morning, and you know it," he insisted.

"Charlie, stop it," I pleaded.

By now I was frantic as he went back by the sink, grabbed a small pan that had some water in it and started tossing water all over the counter with the rest of the mess.

"*Please,*" I begged. "Please, leave it alone and let me clean up this mess. We aren't running out of water, Charlie, there's plenty of water. Please!"

After throwing the pan with the water in it into one of the other pans that was there, he suddenly whirled around and came at me again with his arms flailing to keep me from getting into the kitchen.

Quickly backing up, I moved into the dinette area picked up the phone and called Yvonne. I kept her on the phone for the next half hour while Charlie kept going over to the kitchen sink, grabbing handfuls of ice cubes and throwing them all over the place. Then he'd get water from the tap and slop it into all the pans. Every time I tried to stop him, he'd come at me with fury in his eyes, clenched fists, arms swinging, yelling that we were running out of water.

Yvonne's said she's so afraid that one of these times he might connect when he tries to hit me like he did tonight, and so am I. So far, I've been able to stay out of his way, but I always worry, too, that someday I won't—it's frightening.

~

Carol has been in Arizona for the past two months and is due home tomorrow. Gosh, it seems like she's been gone a year, instead of only a couple of months. I'll be so glad when she gets back. I always feel better when she's around.

Her son Roy, has helped a great deal. He calls me every three or four days to make sure I'm all right, and that in itself has been a blessing.

11

"Where Do I Go From Here?"

March 27, 1994

Sunday. We decided to go see my sister. We haven't been to see her since last summer when Charlie caused so much trouble in the car. Foolishly, I thought that had been just a quirky thing and he'd be all right this time.

The ride over was fine, just like before. We had been there about two hours when suddenly Charlie started to get antsy. He began pacing the floor, and said that if he didn't get out of there he was going to go crazy. Our supper was ready so we ate, but by the time we got finished, he was saying that he felt as if he'd explode and that he wanted to smash everything in sight.

Quickly, and to be on the safe side, I gave him his Haloperidol. Unfortunately, it took about an hour for the pill to take effect, and the ride home was horrifying again.

A couple of times Charlie almost jumped out of the car and I had to slam on the brakes. It's a good thing I had him fastened in with the seat belt. He also started verbally abusing me, just like he had done before.

Everything he said was crazy, accusing me of not giving him enough to eat when we had supper at my sisters, and again telling me he wasn't going to any jail.

One time he held his hat out the window and said he was going to throw it away. Then he said the car was too hot. It wasn't. It was a cold day, and I had the defroster on, but to please him, I shut it off. Then, when the windows started to steam up he accused me of causing it, and opened his window. I was freezing.

By the time we got home I was upset, and sobbing. Yvonne and Braxton were here and I told Yvonne what he had been doing all the way home and Charlie said, "But I didn't hit you, did I?"

March 28

Today Charlie remembered everything he had done yesterday on the way home. He blamed the whole thing on me, telling me *I* was making *his* life miserable.

From one minute to the next I never know what to expect. He may be subdued and quiet, looking to me for direction and asking for my help, then five minutes later he's swearing and verbally abusive.

It's so hard to keep loving someone who isn't really there anymore. I didn't fall in love with just the physical man. I fell in love with the warm-hearted, smiling thoughtful man I used to know.

March 29

I needed a few things from the grocery store, but by the way things were going, I thought I'd either have to ask Yvonne to go for me, or have her watch Charlie while I'd go myself.

This morning he asked me how he could put his pants on. "Here, I'll help you," I said, and I took hold of his pants. "Just put your leg in here," I said, and I held the pant leg out for him.

"I am," he answered.

"No, you're not dear," I said. "You're not lifting your leg."

"I *am* lifting it," he said. But he wasn't. He was just standing there staring at the pant leg I was holding open.

"Come on, honey, you know how to do this," I urged him. "Now just lift your leg and put it in the leg of your pants."

"Damn it, I am!" he shouted.

"Well, if you're going to yell at me," I told him. "I'm not going to help you."

"You've got to help me," he begged. "I can't get them on myself."

So I tried again, but again he just stood there insisting he was lifting it. Disgusted, I reached out and took hold of his leg, hoping I could show him what I wanted him to do.

"Hey, let go of my leg," he yelled, and he kicked at me. Luckily, I managed to get out of his way.

March 30

All day he seemed to be in a fog. This morning he refused to eat his breakfast and I had to talk him into taking his pills.

This afternoon, when he got back from his walk with the neighbor, he looked completely worn out. I tried to get him to lie down and rest, but he was back up in less than a half-hour and for the rest of the afternoon, he did nothing except walk all around the house, saying, "Oh, God, help me, God help me, Junie help me." When he wasn't saying that, he was asking me why I didn't call those people for help. I couldn't figure out what he was talking about. "What people?" I asked.

"I don't know." he said.

~

Tonight he didn't know where the bathroom was and how he was supposed to sit on the toilet.

March 31

At supper time, Charlie complained that his head was hurting him, something he hasn't done for a long time. He also kept saying he felt like he wanted to explode and tear everything to pieces, much the same way he felt the other day when we visited my sister. He was even pounding on the kitchen table, then holding his head.

I gave him his headache medication and it seemed to work because as soon as we finished eating, he went in to lay down. It's 6:10 p.m. and he's still there which is unusual for him.

I'm so worn out, so upset and so tired. I'm also worried because I'm sure Charlie is having more infarcts, only I know there's nothing anyone can do, not even the doctor. I hope that they won't be too bad this time.

April 1

It would be wonderful if just once someone in his family would say to me, "Oh, June, I'm so sorry this happened, or we're with you all the way and we understand." How much that would help. How great it would be to know they were sympathetic in all this.

I wish one of his brothers or sisters would come and take Charlie for a whole day, just so they'd know what it's really like, that it isn't a matter of him just "being forgetful." They have no idea what it's like to live with him. The insanity, the frustration, the sheer strength it takes just to keep going, knowing there's no way out.

Whenever I try to explain his behavior, they always say, "Oh, hey, I do stuff like that all the time." Or else they'll say, "Well, you live with him, you ought to know." To me it's a polite way of saying, "I don't really believe you."

It's hard enough to go through something like this without feeling as if people think I'm making it all up, and exaggerating things, and making mountains out of molehills. At least that's the way it comes across.

~

I try not to think of it, but there are times I still wonder what our "Golden Years" would have been like with the warmth and intimacy that was once our marriage.

~

A writer friend of mine told me I'm an extraordinary woman. Not really, because if I had my way I wouldn't be here. But I have no choice. Where could I go? What could I do? And what would happen to Charlie if I did? I'm not doing this because I want to. I'm doing this because I'm forced to, because there's no other alternative, and I'm stuck with it because I love him.

I try so hard, but I know I fail him a dozen times a day. I try to be patient and loving, but it's so hard when I repeat something ten and fifteen times and he comes right back and asks the same thing again.

How do I keep my cool when he sits and pounds on the table and tells me everything is ugly and terrible when I've knocked myself out trying to make his favorite supper for him? How do I keep from yelling back when he asks me something, I answer him, then he yells, "Shut up your ugly face!", and shakes his fist at me?

If I could find just a little bit of the old Charlie maybe it wouldn't be quite so bad, but he's just not there anymore.

I remember how he'd buzz around the house whistling, singing, and fixing things here and there. How he'd come up behind me, put his arms around me and say, "Boy, honey, supper really smells good tonight."

Charlie was always so full of energy that he made me tired just watching him. Charlie's mind was so quick and sharp and he was such a perfectionist that he was disappointed and frustrated when things didn't go as he planned. We used to tease him and tell him there were three ways to do things, the right way, the wrong way, and Charlie's way.

Sometimes he'd work all night Friday on the "graveyard shift", come home, we'd pack up a picnic lunch, then head for the amusement park. Charlie would spend the day taking the kids on all the rides, even though he wasn't fond of the rides himself. Charlie's life was his kids and he'd do anything to make his girls happy.

And how he always loved to make people laugh, too. I think that's why God gave him big dimples in his cheeks. He was the clown at all the family picnics, and every one of his nieces and nephews called him their favorite uncle.

Charlie was quite a talker. He talked to everyone. Maureen always said she and her father were just alike. If they got on a crowded elevator in a twenty story building, they'd know everybody by the time they reached the top floor. To Charlie, people were always important and interesting and he still tries to talk to people all the time when we're out shopping. Many times he thinks he sees people he used to work with. Sometimes he's right, but most of the time he isn't and I get so embarrassed.

April 2

I know I'm not succeeding in this. I've become a nagging, nasty person. I used to have patience. I used to be warm and loving. Where did my marriage go? Where did all the love go? I don't mean to be nasty, but it just comes out. I feel so frustrated. No one knows unless they go through it.

At one of our support group meetings, one of the women, whose husband had died from Alzheimer's disease, was asked how she felt when he finally passed away. She said one word, "Relieved." I know what she means. The pain is there every day. In your heart, in your every thought and remembrance of what was and what is now.

The madness has a way of grinding you down. Of taking away pleasure in even the little things. I try to laugh, but it doesn't help. It's as if I don't know how anymore. I try to find the humor in things. At first I could, but not anymore. And every day it gets worse. Every day I hate it more. Every day I wonder, when will it ever end? I've always hated to cry, now the tears have become a part of my life, flowing whether I want them to or not.

~

Tomorrow is Easter and I'd love to go to church, but somehow Easter just doesn't hold much excitement for me this year. I remember when the girls were little and instead of having baskets for the Easter Bunny to fill, Charlie made each one of them a beautiful little wooden cart. The carts had long handles and he painted each girl's name on her cart. The girls were so proud of those carts that they kept them over the years and now the grandchildren use them.

Charlie was always the one who hid the eggs for the Easter morning egg hunt. He had a ball hiding those eggs. And sometimes he hid them so well that he forgot how many he hid and we wouldn't find them all until a week or so after Easter. We'd all get such a laugh out of that.

April 4

Charlie has been irritable and edgy all morning. And the names. I've been called so many nasty names and damned to hell so many times. I know it's the disease and not really him, but it doesn't make it any easier to take.

At lunch he threw his Dilantin on the floor, saying he wasn't going to take the pill. He finally took it about an hour later, but by then, I knew I was really in trouble. I thought since he'd taken the Dilantin, he'd take the Haloperidol. No such luck.

I called Yvonne and she talked to him, but he still wouldn't take it. Finally he said, "I'll take it if you have Carol come over and give it to me."

So I called Carol over. However, to my surprise, he treated her badly and wouldn't take it from her either!

After she went home, he looked at me, and his eyes narrowed viciously. "Why did you have that strange lady sneak in here and try to get me to take that nasty pill?"

I was flabbergasted. "That wasn't a strange lady," I told him. "That was Carol."

"Oh no, it wasn't," he yelled at me. "You know damn well it wasn't Carol. You're a sneaky bitch of a liar and I'm going to call somebody and tell them to take care of you. What's our telephone number?"

I told him our number.

"Liar!" he screamed at me again, only this time he took a swing at me with his fist.

I saw his fist coming and quickly leaned back so he just missed my chin. He realized he hadn't connected and started coming after me. I grabbed the cordless phone and ran into the living room, trying to keep out of his reach.

"I'm going to call 911," I yelled, lifting the phone so I could hit the buttons.

Suddenly he straightened up, quit chasing me, grabbed his hat off the couch and said, "I'll fix you. I'm going up to the police station and tell them what a horrible person you are, and what a sneaky, nasty bitch you are."

With that, he marched out the front door and headed up the street on his way to the police station about a half mile from our house.

As soon as he was out of sight and I knew he wasn't going to turn back, I ran over next door to Carol's. She drove up to the police station to warn them he was coming, while I called Dr. Geldmacher to find out what I should do.

The doctor said if Charlie made it to the police station I should have them take him to the emergency room so the doctors there could get him stabilized with medication. So we spent five hours in the emergency room today just because Charlie wouldn't take a pill.

April 5

At Christmas time Jill gave me some lovely coupons good for "Pa sitting". She said that since she wasn't working during the day anymore, every Wednesday will be their day together. I'm really looking forward to cashing in on those coupons starting next week.

Jill is our next to oldest daughter and the other brunette. It's funny really because although Jill was the shortest when she was born, she's now the tallest of all our daughters at five feet seven. The other girls are short like I am. About an inch or so over five feet. I have no idea where Jill gets her height, except Charlie has a couple of brothers who are tall.

Jill is also more independent than the other girls. When she was twenty-one she threw everything she owned into her car and took off for Florida all by herself. Charlie and I were worried sick, but it didn't seem to bother her. She definitely was not the type to hang onto her mother's apron strings. I bet if her kids try to do that when they're twenty-one she'll threaten to kill them!

April 6

The social worker from Dr. Geldmacher's office called today. She said if I didn't find someone to give me some relief more than once or twice a month, I was going to end up sick myself. She also told me to start thinking about what I might have to do to put Charlie in a nursing home. I hate to think of it. For one thing we can't afford it and I know Medicare won't pay for it. There's Medicaid, but I've heard that in order to get that they'd take his social security check. I don't know how true it is, but I couldn't stay in the house without it because I'd need it to pay bills. And if I sold the house, they'd probably want me to put the money into Charlie's care.

Right now I'm hoping we won't have to resort to that but I'm going to find out what my options are, just in case. I'm also going to check into having him put in a Veteran's Administration (VA) nursing home. I've been told since

Charlie is a veteran, it would be the best way to go. In the meantime, I'll just keep him here as long as I can, and hope God will take him before a move is necessary.

April 7

Thank God, I have one more chapter to enter into the computer and the Amish book is finished. Then I'll have to proofread it and that's going to be a bummer unless I can find something for Charlie to do because he's forever interrupting me.

April 8

Another day in never never land. Today was one of those up and down days. The kind that brings anger one minute, pity the next, and makes you wonder where you're going, and how you're going to survive.

This morning while I was standing in the utility room, I saw a robin in the back yard and said a prayer to God. "Please, God, we've lived here almost forty years and the robins have never built their nest in the lilac bush outside our kitchen window. A grackle tried once and we discouraged that, and a cardinal did once, but the babies drowned. The wrens and chickadees have built in the birdhouse that hangs there, but You know how Charlie and I love robins. If You would just have them build their nest in the lilac bush this year, it would give me a sign. Then I'd know that someday, somehow my life will be normal again. That You're with me in all this and that some day it will be over. *Please*, answer my prayer."

❀❀❀

12

"Will There Be An End?"

April 9, 1994

It's not just the big things that wear a person down, it's those little things sandwiched in between. Like when Charlie insists on putting his shoes on the wrong feet. When he refuses to take his pills. When he starts eating out of the serving bowls on the table. When he starts to tell me something, never finishes, then flies into a rage when I have no idea what he's talking about. When he tries to fasten the garbage cans down, asks me to help him, then calls me names and curses at me when I do help.

When he says he's hungry, I cook, then he refuses to eat. When he insists the cold water faucet has hot water coming out of it. When he insists the light is on when it's not. When he insists things are broken and there's not a darn thing wrong with them.

When he says, "June?" I answer, "What?" and he tells me to shut my big fat mouth. When I ask him not to do something, he says he isn't doing it, when he really is. There are so many things.

There are times I just want to scream and ask God why? I can take pain, I can take death and disappointment, but I'm no good at this. I can't take madness and that's what this is, madness.

April 18

I took Charlie to see Dr. Geldmacher today. I told the doctor what has been going on and that I thought Charlie may have had more infarcts. I also told him that ever since Charlie marched off to the police station, and ended up in the hospital emergency room a few weeks ago, he's been holding his right hand in a very strange way. His thumb is very stiff with his fingers curled as if they were claws. And his entire arm is way back by his hip.

The doctor checked Charlie's reflexes, and said Charlie may have had more infarcts or a slight stroke.

While we were there, the social worker told me once again to explore my options and start checking out nursing homes. She said I have to face the fact that Charlie will eventually get worse and need nursing care. I still hate to think of it, but what can I do? So today, I sent for papers to see if I can get him into a nearby VA nursing home.

I just pray that I'll have the strength and courage when the time comes because I know it will be for the best. I know there will be some in his family who will probably condemn me, but then, they haven't had to live with him.

April 22

We sure never know what life has in store for us. It's Friday and it's been a whole week since I felt free enough to sit down and relax.

Our daughter, Maureen, was taken to the hospital on Sunday, and on Monday they diagnosed her with Multiple Sclerosis. She's only forty-three and the doctor said she's had Multiple Sclerosis for about fifteen or twenty years and it was just never diagnosed. All along other doctors had been treating her for other things. In fact, she was kidding around saying she ought to put a big sign up in her front yard that reads, "I told you so!" for all the people who kept telling her she was a hypochondriac.

This has been a shock to all of us, especially to Maureen, but so far she seems to be taking the diagnosis pretty well.

April 26

I have such mixed emotions tonight. I feel so sorry for Charlie. He started crying about 3:45 p.m. and cried all the way up until 5:00 p.m. when we had supper.

For awhile I just sat on the edge of the bed with him, and held him in my arms. While we were sitting there I reached up, took his face between my hands and held it there, looking deep into his eyes. I don't know what I was looking for. Perhaps a spark of the old Charlie, something, anything to give me hope and make me feel better. What I saw though, was a tired, bewildered child. When he started sobbing again, I just gave him a kiss, then let him cry. I felt so helpless.

After supper he started in about his glasses again. From a little after 5:00 p.m. until 7:00 p.m. in the evening he did nothing but clean his glasses, and every once in awhile he'd call me over to look through them. I have no idea what he wanted me to see. The glasses were spotless and each time I'd tell him they were fine, he'd get mad.

April 27

Today Braxton celebrated his 12th birthday. It was also the day Charlie went with Jill, maybe for the last time.

What a fiasco! Charlie had a bath, and was all dressed and ready for Jill to pick him up when he had to go to the bathroom. He is so slow doing things now that he didn't make it to the toilet. So he had a second bath and I got him ready all over again.

The first time Jill took Charlie for the day, he had an accident while they were at the library. I'm glad he was with Jill and not one of the other girls, because Jill took it in stride. She just took him into the men's restroom so she could clean him up, and when one of the male patrons came in and started to say something, she said, "Hey look, my father has dementia, he's had an accident, and I'm taking care of him." That's Jill. Precise, to the point, and no nonsense. There isn't much that embarrasses her.

Today, he had an accident while they were at a discount store. She took him to the restroom and helped him get cleaned up, then instead of going somewhere for lunch, she took him to her house and ordered a pizza.

Shortly after they ate, Charlie started to cry. He wouldn't stop and kept saying he wanted to come home so she had no choice but to bring him home.

We decided that from now on Jill will come out to the house and stay with him and I'll be the one who will go away. I don't know where I'll go, or what I'll do, but I'll find something.

April 30

This morning Charlie told me his dentures needed brushing so I said I'd brush them for him. I was brushing them at the washbowl in the bathroom, when I heard water running in the utility room.

"What are you doing?" I yelled, because I knew Charlie was in the utility room.

"I'm brushing my teeth," he called back.

"You can't be brushing your teeth," I told him, "because I'm brushing them."

"Well now, don't tell me I don't know what I'm doing," he called back. "When I tell you I'm brushing my teeth, I'm brushing my teeth."

Curious by now to see just what he was doing, I stepped into the utility room. He had the hose running in the laundry tub, the one we use when we wash our hair, and he was holding it up so the water was spurting straight up and he had an old toothbrush that he never uses anymore and he was brushing the toothbrush across the top of the hose where the water was coming out.

"See, I told you I was brushing my teeth," he said.

I just went back into the bathroom, finished with his teeth, and put them on the chest of drawers for him.

"Your teeth are ready. You can put them in your mouth now," I called to him.

He came into the bathroom, took one look at his teeth on the dresser and said, "See there, didn't I do a good job cleaning them?" and he put them in his mouth.

Really, it was funny and I couldn't help laughing to myself. It was like the day he was going into the mall with me to buy a lottery ticket but didn't budge from the car.

May 1

Charlie never went to bed until 4:00 a.m. Then he was back in my bedroom at 7:15 a.m. to wake me up.

Last night he would get into bed, stay there for about fifteen or twenty minutes, then get out of bed, come in my bedroom and wake me up. Sometimes he'd turn on the overhead light, then other times he'd turn his flashlight on in my face.

Every time, I'd think he was finally asleep, there he would be, standing beside my bed again saying, "Junie, Junie!"

When I would ask him why he was up and what he wanted he'd always say, "I don't know."

I tried tucking him into bed with kindness, with kisses and hugs. I tried yelling and threatening him, but by 3:00 a.m., I gave up. I went into my office and turned on the computer. I told him I didn't care if he was up or not, but since he wouldn't let me sleep, I might as well get some work done.

Finally, about 3:30 a.m. I heard him climb into bed. As soon as I figured he was asleep, I shut the computer off and went back into bed. I wasn't there for more than fifteen minutes, when suddenly I froze as I heard him getting up again. Seconds later, there he was, standing by my bed asking me what he should do.

"This time I'm not getting up," I told him. "If you want to walk around the house all night that's up to you, but I'm going to get some sleep. Now, go away and leave me alone, I don't ever want to see your face again."

The sad part of it is that I meant it. I was so tired. He wandered around the living room for a while before going back to bed. I laid in bed listening to make sure he didn't get into any trouble while I tried to keep from crying. I don't think I've ever hated anyone the way I hated him last night.

~

After breakfast, he went into the bedroom to lay down. I thought, great, I'll lay down too. Maybe I can catch up on some of the sleep I lost last night.

Forget it. I hadn't even been in bed for five minutes when there he was, right beside my bed saying "Junie wake up." This morning he laid down four times, then I would go lay down too, but each time it was the same thing all over again. So I finally gave up. I guess I'm just not supposed to sleep!

Now he's just walking around the house saying, "Oh, Junie, I don't know, I just don't know."

Well, I know one thing. Right now my heart is breaking. Part of me is so angry I could scream, and part of me wishes I was dead.

He just came over, knelt down by my chair and said, "I'm sorry. So sorry."

"What are you sorry about?" I asked him.

He looked right at me, his eyes all confused. "I don't know," he answered.

This is madness. No one should have to go through this. I feel so alone. . . . God help me! My eyes burn from crying, my head hurts from lack of sleep and my chest hurts from holding back the fury that's taken hold of me. Oh please, God, do something before I break into little pieces.

May 2

I called Dr. Geldmacher's office this morning to find out if there's anything he can prescribe to help Charlie sleep. The nurse said the doctor was out of town and wouldn't be back until later in the week. She said she'd have the doctor call me as soon as he got back. She also said that what I'm feeling, the hate and rage, is only natural. I guess she's right, and she should know.

It isn't much fun or very rewarding to do nice things for a person only to be repaid by indifference and thoughtlessness

He's so wrapped up in himself and his little world that he has no idea, nor does he care, about anything going on around him.

May 3

Today was primary voting day and Yvonne said she'd stop by this afternoon and stay with Charlie so I could vote.

After lunch, Charlie and I were both tired so we laid down to take a nap. The next thing I knew Yvonne was shaking me awake.

"Hey, mom," she yelled, poking me. "Mom, wake up. Did you know dad's up there walking along the boulevard?"

"The boulevard?" I was still half asleep.

"Yeah, he's headed for home, but he's still way up near the custard stand."

"Oh, good Lord," I exclaimed. "I wonder where he's been?"

We never did find out where he'd been. I guess I was just so exhausted I went out like a light, and as soon as I was asleep he took off. He had been gone for almost an hour while I slept, so I guess that stops my catch up naps. I can't have him wandering off like that while I'm sleeping. I just hope I can get him to stay in bed at night or I don't know what I'm going to do. I get so tired.

~

After voting, I came home to pick Charlie up and we went to the bank. On our way back, I asked Charlie if he'd like to eat out for a change. At first he said yes, then changed his mind, and said, "You know I could really go for some fried chicken."

Fine, I thought. So being nice, I figured I'd get a whole bucket of fried chicken. He could have some for supper, then while I was gone Wednesday, he and Jill could have what was left for their lunch.

After paying for the chicken, I was told there would be a ten minute wait. Oh fine. While we were waiting he started acting terrible. He'd been uncontrollable before, but nothing quite as bad as this. He actually wailed and moaned and yelled, and kept hollering, "Oh, Junie, oh God, no! Oh God, Junie, no!"

All the while he was yelling he kept squirming on the seat of the car as if it were on fire or something, lifting himself up off the seat and twisting this way and that. I never saw anyone squirm like that in my life. He was just raising hell.

Even though the full ten minutes wasn't up yet, I got out of the car and went inside. "Could you please hurry," I asked. "I'm having a bit of a problem out there and I just can't wait much longer."

The girl glanced out toward the car. By now Charlie was yelling so loud that everyone could hear him. "I'll have it there in a minute," the girl said.

I went back out and got in the car, hoping to quiet Charlie down. But he wouldn't quiet down. By the time the girl brought the box of chicken out a couple of minutes later, Charlie was howling at the top of his lungs and threatening to rip the roof off the car.

As soon as I started the car moving, he began to quiet down, but he was still moaning and groaning and squirming around. I probably should have gone right home except that I knew that going home wouldn't help. He had yelled and howled like this before, only we were usually at home. So I drove next door to the drive-in to pick up two orders of fries because I know Charlie likes their fries, and then I made one more quick stop to get a hamburger for me because I don't like chicken. But by the time I reached the last drive in, he was wiggling all around in the seat again so hard and yelling and howling so loud that everyone who went by the car was giving me really funny looks.

I was never so glad to finally get home in all my life. As soon as we got home, I gave Charlie his Haloperidol, hoping it would calm him down. Unfortunately, during the hour it took for the pill to work, he only got worse.

When I opened the box of chicken he had a fit, complaining that the chicken was too greasy. Even though he ate a couple of pieces, you would have thought he was being methodically tortured the way he carried on after each bite. He screamed, wailed and howled like a banshee, and nothing I did quieted him down.

Later in the evening Yvonne and Braxton came over. I offered to give them the chicken that was left, figuring Charlie didn't like it, and out of the blue Charlie said, "Hey, don't give that away. I like that chicken, it's damn good."

May 4

Boy, what a dreamer I am. Today's Wednesday, the day Jill is supposed to take care of him and last night was one of the worst nights I've ever experienced in my whole life.

It started out when Charlie pulled the covers out at the bottom of his bed. When I started to tuck them back in for him he grabbed me by the arms and started shaking and shoving me.

"Don't do that!" he yelled.

I managed to break free, only he started coming at me again. "Don't you dare!" I warned him.

The warning seemed to work, but then, about 1:30 a.m. the final straw broke. I had been up and down with him all night, had no sleep the night before, and now, he came into my bedroom and wanted me to get up.

I was so tired, I just told him to go back to his room. Well, he didn't. Instead, he went into the dinette area, and began yelling and hollering at the top of his lungs. It wasn't a normal yell, either. It was more like an agonized wail or howl, the way animals howl at the moon. And it was so loud, it was impossible to ignore.

Then I heard him pick up the kitchen chairs and slam them on the floor as hard as he could. (It's a good thing we have sturdy chairs because they didn't break).

Jumping out of bed, I ran into the living room, which is at the other end of the dining area, and yelled for him to stop. Instead, he hollered all the louder, then turned on me and chased me back into my bedroom.

"Leave me alone!" he screamed. "I'll do what I want." Again he returned to the dinette, and once more began howling and throwing the chairs. Well, the living room was dark, and he was so busy yelling and causing a ruckus, that I managed to sneak to the cordless phone. Grabbing it, I slipped back into my bedroom and dialed 911. I was scared to death.

A few minutes later, when the spotlights from the police cars were shining on the house, to check for the house number, Charlie immediately calmed down. And by the time I went out onto the sunporch and turned the front porch light on for the police officers, Charlie was as docile as a kitten. The officers came in and I told them what he had been doing. Charlie denied everything.

The only thing was, that except for denying doing anything wrong, nothing that Charlie said made any sense. One of the police officers asked me if he was always so incoherent. I told the policemen that Charlie has multi-infarct dementia and they were very supportive. In fact, they told me if anything like this ever happened again, not to hesitate to call. They also stayed at the house with me until I finally got Charlie tucked into bed again.

Not five minutes after the police left, Charlie was up again, only this time there was no howling or throwing chairs. He just kept badgering me all night long. It wasn't until 4:00 a.m. that he finally settled down to sleep.

At 7:25 a.m., he was standing beside my bed waking me. Even though I had only about three hours sleep, I went away today anyway. And I only have one regret, the day went entirely too fast.

~

Before I left this morning, Dr. Geldmacher called. He ordered some sleeping pills for Charlie. I sure hope they work. It's 8:35 p.m. in the evening and I'm going to bed. About 8:00 p.m., I gave Charlie his usual medication and a sleeping pill. He went to bed and so far, he hasn't come out yet.

13

"God Gives Me Hope"

May 5, 1994

Miraculously, the sleeping pills worked last night. I don't know if they're going to keep working every night but even if they don't, I have new hope today.

This morning while I was fixing breakfast, I happened to glance out the window and saw a robin tucking some dried grass into a spot in the lilac bush. She was building a nest, actually building a nest! There were already bits and pieces of twigs there that she was weaving the grass into, and when I realized what she was doing, I began to cry.

The leaves on the bush are just beginning to open. They aren't big enough yet to hide the robin, so I've been able to watch her all morning. Each time I see her heading for the lilac bush, I get tears in my eyes. Not tears of sadness, but of joy, because I know what it means. God has answered my prayer. I'm going to make it through this no matter how long it takes, or how bad it gets, God is with me. He's given me the sign I asked for. Thank you God, thank you with all my heart.

May 6

Just in the past week, I've noticed Charlie is even more hostile and angry.

I'm sitting in the chair next to the fireplace writing in this journal and a few minutes ago he stood in the middle of the living room floor with his back to me and said, "I wish you were dead and your blood and guts were running all over the floor."

I stared at him, then asked, "What did you just say?"

"You heard me," he answered very slowly, and his voice was cold and deliberate, filled with animosity.

I didn't say anything. All I did was sit there staring at his back. I didn't know what to say because a fear like nothing I've ever felt before had suddenly come over me.

Then he turned abruptly toward me. I saw his expression quickly change from one of intense hatred to one of sheepish guilt as he said very contritely, "I'm sorry, I shouldn't have said that, should I?"

"It certainly wasn't a very nice thing to say," I told him.

He sighed. "Then I won't say it again."

What bothers me though is that he said it in the first place. Why would he say something like that unless he was really thinking it? And if he was really thinking it, is there a possibility that he would try to act on those thoughts?

I never thought the day would ever come when I would be frightened of Charlie. Even when he was angry over the years and we'd have words, he never did anything to ever make me think he'd hurt me. But now, I can't help but be petrified.

It's so hard. But the robin is still building her nest and as long as she stays with it, I'll keep my hopes up.

May 8

Mother's Day. Yvonne is going to watch Charlie while I spend the day with my oldest sister. It's Yvonne's Mother's Day present to me, and it means more to me than if she had bought me a gift.

Charlie woke up angry this morning and he's still angry. Even before he had taken his medications, I could just feel the rage emanating from him in everything he said and did. While I was trying to help him get dressed, he was hollering and throwing his shoes all over the bathroom.

"Charlie come in the kitchen now and I'll fix you a nice green pepper omelet for breakfast," I said, then I opened the refrigerator and got out a green pepper.

"I don't want any omelet!" he yelled, and he picked up some things that were on the table and threw them on the floor.

"Then I'll fix you something else." I put the green pepper back in the refrigerator, picked the things up off the floor, then opened the freezer door. "How about some creamed chipped beef on toast?"

"That's better." he said, sounding like an old bear.

He sat down at the table, ready to eat. It took a few minutes to make the toast and warm the chipped beef in the microwave, but he didn't care. He wanted to eat right away, and because it wasn't ready, he sat there pounding on the table with his fist and yelling the whole while I prepared it.

I just hope he calms down enough so Yvonne can handle him. So far I've never worried about leaving Charlie with her because she has a knack for handling him, but since his violent behavior is escalating, there are times when I do worry.

I'm going to give him the Haloperidol the way the doctor suggested, two hours apart until he's had four, and then I hope it works before it's time for me to leave.

May 13

Friday the 13th. How appropriate. He started to go to bed at 8:30 p.m. Thursday night, and it's now 4:00 a.m. Friday morning and he hasn't been to sleep yet. In fact, now he's taken his pajamas off, put his pants on, and he's asking me to fix him his breakfast. Well, he isn't going to get breakfast at this hour!

He keeps asking me what to do. I tell him to take his pants off and go back to bed. He says he can't do that. Thank God he isn't violent or abusive tonight. He's acting more like a zombie and he's fighting sleep like a drowning man fights water.

May 14

It's 1:30 a.m. Saturday morning and I've been up since Thursday morning without any sleep. I even called Dr. Geldmacher yesterday and he gave me new instructions for the sleeping pills. They aren't working. Charlie won't even let me sleep during the day. Every time he lays down, I sneak into my bedroom and lay down too. My head barely hits the pillow, before he's beside me, telling me I have to get up.

Yvonne will be here on Sunday to wash clothes, and maybe I can figure out a way to get some sleep. If I can just hang on until then. Right now, I wish I could kill him, because I'm so tired I can hardly keep my eyes open.

~

It's early evening. Charlie's still up, walking around saying, "Oh, God help me," over and over again.

I've been trying to catnap every chance I can get, and I just hope it will be enough in case he's up again all night.

~

Now he's pacing the house and mumbling to himself.

"What's the matter?" I asked him.

"Well, I can't find anything," he answered.

"Like what?"

"The eyes, the box," he said. "You know, all that stuff."

I just shook my head.

~

I have been trying to reach Dr. Geldmacher all day to let him know the new instructions with the sleeping pills don't work. I finally managed to reach the doctor who is on call for the weekend. She was so nice, so sympathetic, and I have more instructions for the medicine. Shortly after I hung up, Dr. Geldmacher called to make sure I understood the instructions from the other doctor. Dr. Geldmacher's so thoughtful and concerned, even when he's not on call.

May 15

Charlie finally conked out at 3:30 a.m. and did let me sleep until 8:00 a.m., but I'm still so tired. I tried to catch up on some sleep while Yvonne was here today, but every time I would go in my bedroom and shut the door, Charlie would wait until Yvonne's back was turned, then sneak in and wake me up.

May 16

Last night was a repeat of Saturday night and I got to sleep at 4:45 a.m. Thankfully we both slept until 9:00 a.m. I can't function on so little sleep, and I don't think he can either. Charlie fights sleep as if it were the plague. I have no idea what keeps him going.

This morning Dr. Geldmacher's nurse called to find out if the sleeping pills were working. She called when I was having a terrible time with Charlie and I was crying and upset. She said his staying up all night and his demands on me, are jeopardizing my health. She said it sounds like he needs twenty-four hour supervision.

I told her I've decided to try to get him into one of the VA nursing homes and that I received the application forms a few days ago. I said I would complete the forms today and send them to the doctor so he could sign them.

I talk about having to put him in a nursing home. I know that day will come, and I know that even though it'll be for the best, it will tear my heart out. I only hope that when the day comes that I sit in this house alone, I'll be strong enough to accept it.

I don't want to see Charlie go. If they can just find a way to make him sleep all night so that I can get some sleep, I don't mind taking care of him. I really don't. It isn't any fun, and it isn't easy, but I can handle it. That is as long as my health holds out.

May 20

The robin's nest is finished and she's already nesting. I see her go in and out of the lilac bush every once in awhile and I can hardly wait to hear the chirping when the birds are hatched and she starts to feed them. Believe me, that robin's nest is the only thing that's been keeping me going these past few weeks.

~

It looks like I'm going to have to change Charlie's meals. Tonight I fixed some corn on the cob. I figured it was a way to please Charlie because he always loved corn on the cob. He wasn't pleased, instead, he had a fit and called it sloppy pig food, and said he'd never eat it again. I also fixed chicken thighs and had a hard time keeping him from eating them bones and all. I guess I'll have to get boneless chicken or chicken patties from now on.

~

This evening, I went to a program for caregivers while Yvonne stayed with Charlie. There were lectures given by experts on Alzheimer's and other dementias. The talks were informative, but I think those of us who go to these programs want miracles, and there are none. I think we all expect to come home with clear cut answers for what's happening in our lives and a sure way to handle our problems.

I asked one of the speakers, "How will we know when it's time to put someone in a nursing home?"

"Don't worry," he said. "You'll know."

May 23

I just made it through another horrible weekend. Charlie was up all night Friday night and all Saturday night. Early this morning I sat on the sunporch, so tired and weary I could hardly think straight. With tears streaming down my face, I watched the dawn begin to creep into the night sky, and the birds in the marsh awaken to a new day.

I talked to Dr. Geldmacher's nurse a short while ago and she said before the doctor signs the papers for Charlie to go into the nursing home, he wants to see if some of the medication that Charlie is taking might be causing some of his mental confusion. So he wants to take Charlie off of all his medications except the Dilantin, for three days over the Memorial Day weekend that's coming up. However, he said I can't be alone with Charlie when I do this, so Yvonne is going to stay with me while Braxton stays at Jill's house.

The doctor said that if, during the three days, Charlie becomes violent to the point where we can't control him, I should give him some medication, call 911, and have him taken to the local hospital emergency room. There I should ask the emergency room doctor to transfer Charlie to the psychiatric hospital next door. From there, Dr. Geldmacher will have Charlie transferred to University Hospital in Cleveland. So that's what we have planned.

May 24

Charlie still won't sleep. I can't even work on the computer anymore when Charlie has me awake during the night because last night he banged on the walls and hollered something terrible. Now all I do is sit up in the chair in the living room and watch the hours go by. If I were to go to bed and go to sleep, leaving him wandering around without supervision, I could easily wake up to a disaster. Or not wake up at all because he accidently set the house on fire or something.

~

Charlie continues to get worse. He can't dress himself at all anymore. Earlier today he took a clean pair of socks out of his drawer and blew his nose on them. I've seen him eat his toast with a spoon, try to use his fork to get a taste of coffee from his coffee cup, and last night he was trying to eat his beef noodle soup without a spoon, holding the soup bowl up to his mouth, trying to snare the noodles with his teeth. This morning I found his flashlight in the refrigerator, and I've found canned goods in the freezer.

There is no more of my old Charlie left. All I see is a bewildered, mixed up old man. And yet he's not old. He'll be sixty-seven in a few weeks and physically he's still in good health. In fact, he's as strong as he ever was.

I've loved Charlie until it hurt. Until I thought I'd die inside. People may condemn me for wishing so many times that he was dead already, but those condemning me never had to live it. They never had to cope with the insanity of it. But God knows. He knows what's in my heart. He knows how much I hate myself when I let the madness get to me. He knows how I dread each day, and why. He also knows that I'm only human, and He is forgiving.

Right now though, I'm going to have to be strong enough to get through tonight because I have a horrible feeling he isn't going to want to go back to bed, and I'm so very tired.

May 25

I took Charlie to the store with me today because I had no one to leave him with, but I'm never going to do that again. I had a hard time watching him because he kept wandering. When we were at the fruit market, he tried to push another man's cart, then he got mad when the man tried to stop him. I was so embarrassed as I tried to explain to the man and apologize.

~

Last night, one thing happened that was really hilarious. Charlie was still wandering around at 11:00 p.m. when I saw him take a bag of pretzels off the top of the refrigerator and sit down at the kitchen table to eat them. I didn't pay much attention to him because he often does that, so I continued watching television.

When the program was over, I went into the kitchen. There, on the counter, were Charlie's slippers. I stopped, stared at the slippers, and wondered why they were there. When I turned on the overhead light, I discovered that one of the slippers was just stuffed full of pretzels. I stood there for a moment staring at the slipper, then started to laugh. Charlie laughed, too.

14

"I'm Forced To Let Go"

May 30, 1994

Monday, Memorial Day. Our three day experiment with Charlie is almost over. What a time Yvonne and I have had. It's proved one thing though, the medications have *not* been the cause of Charlie's problems. He's just as bad, if not worse, without medication as he is when he was taking it.

Now Charlie does nothing but walk, walk, walk, around the house, outside the house, anywhere he can walk. Last night, he was sweating so badly from all the walking, I gave him a towel to wipe himself off .

When I tried to stop him and make him sit down for a few minutes, he said, "I can't." And he said it emphatically, letting me know not to try to stop him again. He's still walking today, shuffling along, wiping the sweat off as he goes.

Since Saturday morning, Charlie has become more difficult to control. He's more agitated, more testy, and at times, downright nasty and mean.

Saturday night Charlie refused to go to bed and he was up all night. I let Yvonne sleep while I stayed up with him, then at 6:00 a.m. Sunday morning, I fixed breakfast and watched the sun come up again. Later, when Yvonne got up, I went to bed. I slept until noon.

Since it was a holiday weekend, Yvonne and I thought we'd pretend things were normal around here and decided to grill hamburgers on the charcoal grill. We don't use the gas grill, because Charlie keeps wanting to use lighter fluid to light it.

The hamburgers turned out beautifully, but Charlie kept insisting we were trying to poison him. I also made some potato salad and when he saw the hamburger and potato salad on his plate, and saw us putting ketchup and pickles on our hamburgers, he threw up his arms and started to flail them all around in the air yelling, "Oh no! Oh my God!" Then he grabbed his head and moved it from side to side while yelling. "I can't eat this piggish mess. Why are you trying to feed me this messy slop? Oh my God, no, no, no!"

Both of us tried to explain to him that there was nothing wrong with the food, but he wouldn't listen. Finally, we gave him a plain hamburger on a bun and he did eat that. But the whole while he was eating it, he kept protesting.

He went to bed about 11:30 p.m. last night and thank God, he slept until 7:00 a.m. It wasn't a breakthrough but, I think it was more the fact that he was completely worn out after no sleep the two nights before, and from the constant walking.

Jill dropped Braxton off while we were eating supper. Braxton was tired, so he went into my bedroom to lie down. Charlie was making a fuss about the food again and he even picked up his dish and threatened to throw it across the room. He finally sat down to eat some watermelon, and while he was eating, I took out the trash.

As I was coming in the back in the house, I heard Yvonne crying and hollering, "No, no, don't hit me again."

Dropping the wastebasket, I hurried into the living room. "Did you hit Yvonne?" I asked him.

"Shut up," he said. "Or I'll hit you too," and he started to come at me.

Right away, I ran to get his medications. What I didn't know was that Yvonne had been talking to Maureen on the phone when Charlie hit her, and Maureen had called the police.

At first Charlie wouldn't take the pills, but when he heard Yvonne say that Maureen had called the police, he quickly changed his mind.

Before the police arrived, I asked Yvonne why Charlie had hit her. She said all she did was ask him not to go into my bedroom and wake up Braxton.

By the time the police got here, Charlie was starting to calm down, only I don't think it was because of the medicine. I think Charlie had enough fear of the police coming, to know he was doing something wrong.

When the police and the rescue squad arrived, the paramedics took Charlie's blood pressure. It was 208 over 110, so he ended up in the hospital emergency room.

May 31

I honestly think something happened to Charlie in the emergency room last night because while he was lying on the gurney. I saw that he was trembling and I thought he was chilled so I asked for a blanket. I put it over him, but his skin felt warm.

I also noticed that the monitor showed his pulse rate was up to 136. I brought it to the nurses attention, but she didn't seem too concerned.

When we first arrived, I talked to the emergency room doctor and told her exactly what Dr. Geldmacher's instructions had been to me. Well, the doctor didn't seem to be concerned at all about Charlie's mental state. All she was concerned about was the fact that she found nothing physically wrong with him, and after all the testing was done, I overheard her talking to the neurologist who was on call. She didn't tell the neurologist any of Dr. Geldmacher's instructions I had relayed to her. Instead, the emergency room doctor simply said that Charlie had been brought there and there was nothing physically wrong with him except that his blood pressure had been high, but was now under control.

By this time, Charlie was no longer lying on the gurney trembling, instead he was sitting up, trying to rip the IV out of his arm, and wrestling with me, as I was struggling with him to keep him on the gurney. I was having such a difficult time with him that the nurse called security to come in and quiet him down and keep him from hurting himself or me.

That's when the emergency room doctor came in. "You can take him home now," she said.

I was astonished. "You mean you're going to have me take him home in this condition?" I asked her. "His doctor wanted him sent to the mental hospital next door."

"I don't have any authority to send him next door," she replied, and she sounded rather irritated with me. "And there's nothing physically wrong with him so I can't keep him here. I've already signed his release, so you're going to have to take him home."

I couldn't believe it. She was sending him home. A man who was still keeping the guards busy while he tried to rip the IV out of his arm, a man who wasn't listening to a word anyone was saying to him, and she was sending him home.

"You go get your car and bring it around to the emergency room door. We'll see that your husband gets out to the car," one of the guards told me.

I just stared at Charlie and there were tears in my eyes. "I can't take him home like this," I said.

"You're going to have to," one of the nurses said. "We can't keep him here. The doctor already signed the release."

So while the nurse and the security guards continued to fight with Charlie to get the IV out of his arm, and get him safely off the gurney, I went outside to get the car and drove up to the emergency room entrance.

Just as I pulled up, the two security guards came out pushing Charlie in a wheelchair. It took them almost fifteen minutes to get Charlie out of the wheelchair and into the car, where we fastened him in with the seat belt.

By now, it was half past midnight. There was little traffic so it took me only about fifteen minutes to get home. All the way, I prayed through my tears that I'd be able to handle him once we got home. I pulled into the garage and parked the car. Charlie refused to get out. After pleading and begging for a while, I managed to get him out of the car and headed toward the house. He kept saying he had to go to the bathroom, and he was determined to do it right in the driveway. I pushed and shoved him toward the house while he flailed his arms trying to keep me away. Inch by inch, I kept him moving until we finally made it to the door.

As soon as I got him inside, I took him to the bathroom, then into his bedroom. I had just seated him on the edge of the bed, when the doorbell rang.

To my surprise it was two Mentor-on-the-Lake police officers. Charlie was so bad when we left the hospital that the security guards took the initiative to call the police. The guards were afraid I'd have a problem trying to get Charlie into the house and they didn't want me to get hurt.

After telling the police officer the problem I had getting Charlie into the house, they stayed with me while I got him tucked into bed, and I thanked them for that. They said if I had any more problems to just give them a call.

Five minutes after they left, Charlie got up and kept me up until 4:00 a.m. So much for the doctor's experiment. Charlie is back on full medication again, and I'm running on three hours sleep.

June 1

When I called Dr. Geldmacher yesterday morning and told him what had happened at the emergency room, he was furious. He said he would sign the papers for the VA nursing home.

It's now 1:00 a.m. Wednesday. I don't know what to do anymore. There's nowhere to turn. I try to remember my robins nest and keep my hopes up, telling myself there will be an end to it some day, but when?

I feel like I'm breaking into little pieces, and to top it off Charlie thinks everything is funny. When I cry he mocks me and makes fun of me, and he seems to think it's funny when I tell him to go to bed and go to sleep. Dr. Geldmacher said he's what's called a "sundowner." He'll stay up three or four days in a row, then sleep one night which is usually long enough to recoup his energy, then he'll stay up for three or four more days. And then to make matters worse, when the sun goes down and it's dark outside, his mental confusion escalates.

He's been sitting on the edge of his bed for hours now just taking his slippers off and putting them back on again, as if it's some sort of special ritual.

I feel like I'm as much a prisoner here as Charlie because when I try to leave the house without him, he becomes violent.

Every time I start to question myself and think that I should try to keep him at home longer, something horrendous happens. I realize that just because we have a few good moments, it doesn't mean that things will ever be normal again, and it's usually the calm before the storm.

~

It's late Wednesday evening now as I write this. I sat in the armchair in the living room and prayed between the tears as I watched the hours go by and Charlie wandered around the house. He finally went to bed at 3:00 a.m. When I laid down, I felt as if I were dying.

It was 8:00 a.m. when I was awakened abruptly by Charlie standing next to my bed hollering, "Where's my breakfast?" and he sounded like it was an ultimatum for a battle or something.

I got out of bed immediately because I knew something was wrong.

"I want my breakfast," he demanded.

Right away, I started to fix breakfast. Then I got out his medication but Charlie didn't want to take the pills.

"If you want your breakfast you'd better take them," I said.

To my surprise he did, and I breathed a sigh of relief because I hoped they'd calm him down. They didn't. There was a tenseness and hostility in his manner that warned me he was right on the verge of really getting violent, and I wasn't about to cross him. I could see it in his eyes. It was as if he was challenging me.

He kept pestering so much about the food not being ready that I finally told him to go sit on the sunporch.

Surprisingly he did, but every once in awhile he would yell like some scary ogre, "Where's my food?".

When it was ready I called him, but when he got to the table, he said, "I thought you said there was food here."

There was a plate with a green pepper omelet, slice of toast, glass of juice and a cup of coffee. "There it is, that's your breakfast," I said.

"That's not my food!" he screamed.

I was flabbergasted, yet knew I had to try to appease him somehow. "Well, maybe it's sitting in the wrong place," I said as I picked up the dish and moved everything around to the side of the table where I usually sit.

He sat down, picked up his fork and stabbed the slice of toast with it, then tried to shove the whole thing into his mouth all at once.

"No, honey," I tried to explain. "The whole slice won't fit in your mouth."

"Shut up!" he yelled. "I know what I'm doing. I'll eat it any way I damn well please!"

His eyes were wild looking, and while he was trying to shove me away and get the whole slice of toast into his mouth, both at the same time, he knocked his plate off the table and there was omelet all over the kitchen floor at his feet.

I tried to get him to move so I could clean it up, but he wouldn't budge. Instead, he started swinging at me with his fists. I managed to stay out of his way, but I went into the pullman kitchen, got some paper towel and came back into the dinette area to try to wipe the mess up. He still wouldn't let me get near it.

He was still sitting on the chair, but he was leaning over, his right fist swinging at me to keep me away, while he used his left hand to scoop the omelet off the floor and shove it into his mouth.

I was sobbing uncontrollably by this time, and I ran for the phone, and called the doctor.

"Can you take him to University Hospital's emergency room?" he asked me.

"I'll get him there if I have to have them take him in a private ambulance," I told him.

After I hung up, I was at a loss and I just stood there crying because I didn't even know where the hospital was, except that it was somewhere in Cleveland.

Meanwhile, the front doorbell rang and it was Roy from next door coming to see if we were all right. When he saw what was happening, he tried to help me get Charlie to settle down. Charlie didn't seem to hear, or pay any attention to anything we were saying or doing.

I told Roy that I had to get him to University Hospital's emergency room, he said he'd take us. I was so relieved.

By the time we arrived at the hospital a little after noon, Charlie was unable to walk by himself and they had to take him into the emergency room in a wheelchair. All the way there and when we first got there Charlie was so quiet and docile.

However, when Roy went to get the car later to take me home, Charlie started trying to get off the gurney. I tried to get him to lie still, however, he looked right at me, gritted his teeth and said real loud, "Shut up your big fat mouth!"

The nurse saw what was happening and heard what Charlie had said to me. She said, "You go along, Mrs. Shiplett, and don't worry. We'll handle him from now on."

I just stared at Charlie for a minute with tear-filled eyes, then I slowly turned, and walked out of the emergency room. I didn't even look back. I just couldn't.

Thank God they've admitted him and that's where he is now. I don't know what's going to happen, but I do know he's finally in a place where he can get help.

June 2

Until today, it seems like I haven't stopped running since Charlie went into the hospital. I still don't think I can relax though because I'm so afraid they're going to send him home, and he's impossible for me to handle anymore.

I went to see Charlie this evening and while I was there, the nurse gave me a consent form to fill out about life support systems. I am to read it over and let the doctors know what I want done, just in case anything should happen.

At the time the nurse gave me the consent form, I told her that Charlie and I had often discussed that very thing. He always said, and I agreed with him, that if at any time either of us had brain damage and our minds were gone so we had no quality of life left, that neither of us would let the other be kept alive by artificial means.

Charlie and I had visited a lot of nursing homes. We've seen so many people being kept alive when it would have been much more merciful to just let them die. Whenever we'd see them, Charlie would always say, "Honey, if I'm ever in that condition and I can't enjoy life and my family anymore, whatever you do, don't ever let them fight to keep me alive. Just let me go so I can die with dignity."

When I got home, I started calling the girls so we could talk over the consent form. Each had remembered hearing their father say the same thing, so they agreed with my decision not to have anything done which would include intravenous feedings.

However, before I could call Yvonne, she called me. While we were talking, the operator cut in and said she had an emergency call for my line.

We hung up right away and a call was put through from a doctor at the hospital. He said Charlie had been complaining of chest pains so they had given him a cardiogram which showed irregular heart activity. The nurse remembered what I had told her earlier, and because they didn't want me to come in and perhaps find him hooked up to a life support system, they asked me if there was any way I could get the form to them tonight.

It was after 10:00 p.m. and with the hospital some thirty miles away, I didn't know what to do. The doctor then asked if I could find a fax machine somewhere and fax it. I told him I'd try to locate one and I'd get back to him right away.

I figured if anyone knew where a fax machine was, it would be Maureen, so I called her. While I was waiting for her to call back, I filled out the form. Sure enough, she called and said that one of the local hospitals would fax it through for me. So there I was at 10:30 p.m., rushing to the hospital that was about fifteen minutes from the house.

Fortunately they didn't need to use the consent form that night because the chest pains stopped and Charlie felt fine, but if they had needed it, it was there.

That's where we are now. They won't have any of the results of the tests they've been taking until Monday or Tuesday. So until then everything is still in limbo. I don't know what's ahead for us, but I do know that taking Charlie to the hospital was the right thing to do.

June 7

It's been a week since Charlie went into the hospital. The tests are completed and I talked to the doctor today. He said Charlie has massive brain damage from multi infarcts and his condition is irreversible. He is in such bad shape that he doesn't recognize any of us when we go see him. Not even me. The doctor said Charlie will never be able to come home again.

I sit here in the evenings looking around the house and I try to remember how it used to be before all this happened, it's so hard.

June 10

Tonight I was thinking about Charlie. I remembered a funny thing that happened a week or so before he went into the hospital. It was one of those rare nights when he managed to sleep off and on. At about 4:00 a.m., he woke up, and I went to see what was the matter. He was really frightened and disoriented. He didn't seem to want to be alone, so I said, "Wait a minute and I'll go get my pillow and climb in bed with you."

Usually when I say that he says, "No, no, you don't have to, I'll be all right," so I don't.

But that night I didn't even wait for him to say anything because he seemed too scared, so I just went and got my pillow, then came back and climbed into bed with him.

There's a picture of me on the wall up over Charlie's night stand. It's a picture that was taken about ten years ago when my hair was long and full, and didn't have gray in it.

While we were lying there, I was talking to him, telling him how much I loved him and trying to comfort him, when suddenly he pointed to the picture on the wall.

"See that picture?" he said. "That's a picture of my wife."

"I know," I answered, and I smiled and I wrapped my feet around his affectionately.

Suddenly he said, "You know, I think you'd better go."

"You want me to go?" I asked.

"Yeah, you'd better go. I'll be all right now."

I was a little surprised but when he assured me that he'd be just fine, and seemed to be so insistent that I leave, I picked up my pillow, tucked him in, gave him a kiss, and went back to my own bed.

The next afternoon, we were out in the back yard sitting at the picnic table when he looked at me and said, "Where did we go last night?"

"We didn't go any place," I answered.

"Oh yes, we did," he insisted, and he was dead serious, his face all red with embarrassment. "We went somewhere during the night and some strange elderly lady climbed into bed with me and was kissing me."

I was floored. Every time I think of it, I have to laugh. How weird the mind is. How intricate and delicate a thing it is. And how strange that after forty-four years of marriage I've suddenly been shut out. I'm still a part of his life and yet I'm not. The June he calls for now is the same June he married, but the gray hair, weight gain, wrinkles and signs of age are not the June he remembers marrying.

He remembers me as I used to be, and that's all right because even though he doesn't remember that I'm his wife and we've grown old together, I know deep down in his heart, he still loves me, otherwise he wouldn't have been so worried about the elderly lady crawling into bed and kissing him.

June 13

Today when I went to see Charlie in the hospital, he actually recognized me. Not as his wife. I never expected that because he hasn't recognized me as his wife for over a year now. But when I walked into the lounge at the hospital, he was sitting in the wheelchair and he pointed to me and he said, "Hey."

I walked over, said, "Hi," and he said, "Hi," back.

"How about a kiss?" I asked him.

He raised his head and puckered his lips. It was the first time he ever did that in the hospital, and the first time in months he has responded like that, so I gave him a big kiss.

Then I looked down into his eyes and asked, "Do you know who I am?"

He studied me for a few seconds. "June?" he answered.

"That's right," I said. "And do you know who June is?"

He studied me some more. "No, but I love you."

"I love you, too," I said, and the tears began to flow.

~

The VA turned Charlie down. They said his mind is too badly damaged and they wouldn't be able to keep him confined, which is what he needs. They also said with his propensity to violence he would be too disruptive, so we've had to find another place for him.

The tears are there now as I write this because I know what tomorrow is going to bring and even though I've been prepared for it, it will be so hard. How do I let go of a part of my life that meant so much? And I have to let go, for his sake as well as mine.

June 14

Late this afternoon Charlie was transferred by ambulance from University Hospital to a nursing home in Andover, Ohio, where Maureen and I were waiting. I turned him over to others who will help him on his way. We stayed with him for awhile to help him get settled, then I had to let go.

~

It's 10:00 p.m. now. The tears are here again because our journey together is finally over. And there are so many tears. Tears of sadness, of guilt, of relief, of what we had and what we've lost, tears so deep they flood my soul. Charlie and I have come to a bend in the road and he's going to have to go around that bend without my help. From here on I will only be a visitor in Charlie's world. Though our lives are no longer spent with each other, the love we once shared can never be dimmed or blotted out by the horrors of our journey. The love that is somehow remembered, even through the bad times, as the way it used to be.

AFTERWORD

I left my heart in that nursing home back in June of 1994, and the tears still come often. How quiet the house is. How lonely at times, and yet there are still so many memories that haunt me.

Charlie was in the Andover nursing home for only ten days before we were able to move him to the AlterCare Health Care Center right here in Mentor, Ohio where he is now. It's only a fifteen minute ride from my house, and it's a beautiful place. The staff take such good care of Charlie and the people there are like one big family.

For the first few months he was in the nursing home, I had to pay for his care. It took most of the little money we had managed to save over the years, but now Medicaid has taken over. I still have my house, and although things have been rough at times, I'm surviving with God's help.

Charlie's hair is what people would call salt and pepper now and physically he's doing quite well, although he's lost a great deal of weight because he doesn't eat like he used to. Some of the infarcts have healed and at times he knows who some of us are again, but his mind is still so terribly mixed up.

He still has a few infarcts off and on and for awhile he didn't know who we were again. Now he seems to be doing a little better although he can't feed himself anymore and has to be diapered.

I'm slowly getting my life back in order. I attend church regularly and find that I'm able to join in the fellowship. I continue to go to support group meetings because I still need them, but what pleases me the most, is that I am back to writing and networking with my writing friends.

I don't visit Charlie every day, I can't, it's too hard on me emotionally. I go about every three days and the children try to visit on the days when I don't go. Brittany, who's married now, takes our little great-grandson to see Charlie. Charlie's eyes always light up when he sees him, and he grins from ear to ear.

Most of the time when I'm there I just sit and hold Charlie's hand and tell him how much I love him because he seems to like that. And I can love him again now because I have quality time with him. Sometimes I help him play bingo with the other patients, and once a month the minister from our church comes to the nursing home and when Charlie is able, we take communion together.

When I leave one of the aides helps him stand by the window overlooking the parking lot. He waves and throws me kisses and by the time I wave to him for the last time and head for the main road, the tears are usually streaming down my cheeks.

Charlie has never asked to come home, but then I doubt he knows where home is.

SUGGESTED READING

WHERE TO GO FOR HELP

GLOSSARY

SUGGESTED READING

With the growing number of Americans afflicted with dementia of one sort or another, more books are being written. Some tell a caregiver's story or relay personal experiences while others are written by professionals as educational references. There are books specifically written for children like *Grandpa Doesn't Know It's Me* by Donna Guthrie, and *Everything You Need To Know When Someone You Love Has Alzheimer's Disease* by Joyce Hinnefeld.

Each of these books provides a unique perspective and helps to educate and foster a greater understanding of this dreadful illness and its effect on family and the community.

Be sure to visit your local library as well as contact organizations within your community, especially your local Alzheimer's Association, for books, tapes, videos, support groups, and educational programs that may interest you and address your specific needs. The following books are ones I found most helpful:

THE LOSS OF SELF: A Family Resource for the Care of Alzheimer's Disease and Related Disorders by Donna Cohen, Ph.D., and Carl Eisdorfer, Ph.D., M.D., W.W. Norton & Company, New York (1987).

> *A comprehensive resource for family and friends of those with Alzheimer's Disease. Covers every aspect of the disease and profiles the role of a caregiver.*

THE 36 HOUR DAY: A Family Guide to Caring for Persons with Alzheimer's Disease, Related Dementing Illness and Memory Loss in Later Life by Nancy L. Mace, M.A. and Peter V. Rabins, M.A., Ph.D., The Johns Hopkins University Press, New York, (1981, revised 1991).

> *This book is a* ***must*** *for anyone caring for someone with dementia.*

LIVING IN THE LABRYNTH: A Personal Journey Through the Maze of Alzheimer's by Diana Friel McGowin, Bantam Imprint of Doubleday, New York (1994). Also available in large print from Thorndike Press, Unity, Maine.

Chronicles one woman's experience through the early stages of dementia, diagnostic evaluation, and the impact of cognitive problems in her every day life. An excellent book for understanding the terror of the disease from a victim's point of view.

WHEN ALZHEIMER'S HITS HOME by Jo Danna, Ph.D., Palomino Press, Briarwood, New York (1995).

The first part of this book is an eloquently told story of the author as her mother's caregiver with insight into the actions and situations that occur with one who has Alzheimer's disease. The second part is a sourcebook for caregivers. Very informative, highly recommended.

WHERE TO GO FOR HELP

Alzheimer's Disease & Related Disorders Association
919 North Michigan Avenue, Suite 1000
Chicago, Illinois 60611-1676
800/272-3900

Excellent source for books, tapes, videos; educational programs, counseling resources to families and caregivers; moral support; hot line; support groups; newsletter; free publications. There are local chapters throughout the U.S., and similar organizations in most industrialized countries.

American Heart Association
7272 Greenville Avenue
Dallas, Texas 75231-4596
800/242-8721 • 214/373-6300

Provides information about strokes, support groups; acts as a referral service; heart health; nutrition.

Health Care Finance Administration
Health & Human Services Department
200 Independence Avenue S.W., 314 G
Washington, D.C. 20201
202/690-6726

Information about Medicare and Medicaid

National Institute of Neurological Disorders & Stroke
National Institutes of Health
9000 Rockville Pike
Bethesda, Maryland, 20892
301/496-5751

Information about stroke, support for stroke survivors and their families.

National Hospice Organization
1901 N. Fort Myer Drive, Suite 902
Arlington, Virginia 22209
703/243-5900

National Institute on Aging
Information Center
P.O. Box 8057
Gaithersburg, Maryland 20898
800/222-2225

Literature on health topics for older people. Write or call for the "Publications List."

National Institute on Aging
Alzheimer's Disease Education and Referral
ADEAR Center
P.O. Box 8250
Silver Springs, Maryland 20907-7250
800/438-4380

Provides free information regarding disease, diagnosis, treatment resources and research; referral agency.

Social Security Office
Social Security Administration
6401 Security Boulevard
Baltimore, MD 21235
800/772-1213
410/965-3120

Veterans Affairs Department
Veterans Benefits Administration
810 Vermont, N.W., Mail Code 27
Washington, DC 20420
202/273-2761 • 202/418-4343

GLOSSARY

Angiogram: Radiography examination of blood vessels following an injection of a radiopaque substance (dye). A cerebral angiogram is an x-ray of blood vessels supplying the brain including the portions outside the skull.

Alzheimer's Disease: is the most common type of dementia affecting older people. It results from premature death of brain cells. The cause is not known. *(see dementia)*

Blood Tests: Routine blood tests help in evaluating a person's overall health condition and are performed as part of the diagnostic evaluation. For dementia, they usually include blood counts; kidney, liver, and thyroid function; vitamin B12 levels; and tests for syphilis.

CAT Scan (Computerized Axial Tomography): An x-ray image obtained by examination with a CAT Scanner used to confirm the diagnosis of dementia.

CAT Scanner: A tomographic device employing narrow beams of x-rays in two planes at various angles to produce computerized cross-sectional images of the body, including soft tissues like the brain.

Dementia: A general mental deterioration due to the result of degeneration and death of brain tissue or psychological factors characterized by distortion of thought, impaired memory, diminished judgement, and loss of intellectual abilities severe enough to interfere with social or occupational functioning.

EEG (Electroencephlogram): A recording of the electrical impulses of the brain derived from electrodes attached to the skull. Sometimes referred to as a brain wave test.

Infarct: An area of tissue that is dying or is dead from suddenly being deprived of its blood supply.

MRI (Magnetic Resonance Imaging): A neurological scan of the brain which permits an in-depth view of all brain tissue, regardless of intervening bone, by means of a strong magnetic field and low-energy radio waves. The procedure produces a film which illustrates "slices" of the brain for close examination and review by the doctors. Similiar to the CAT scan, it may provide information on localization of degeneration of brain tissue and aid in the diagnosis and cause of illness. It can "see" smaller or more subtle changes than the CAT scan.

Medications:

- **Diazepam (Valium):** A skeletal muscle relaxant, sedative, and anti-anxiety agent.
- **Haloperidol (Haldol):** A widely used high potency tranquilizer which reduces symptoms of agitation, anxiety, and related insomnia.
- **Lorazepam (Adivan):** An anti-anxiety agent similar to Diazepam, but removed from the body more quickly, a minor tranquilizer.
- **Nortriptyline (Pamelor):** An anti-depressant.

Multi-Infarct Dementia (MID)/Vascular Dementia: A step-like deterioration of intellectual functions with focal neurological signs as the result of multiple "infarcts"or breakdowns of the vascular system within the brain, such as both minor and major strokes.

ABOUT THE AUTHOR

A story about a time-travel romance, and a letter of encouragement from "Dear Abby," got June Lund Shiplett started on a successful writing career. During the past twenty years, June has seen fifteen of her books published by New American Library, Pocketbooks, and Harlequin Historicals, with combined sales reaching more than three million.

A member of the Romance Writers of America, June is very active with the Northeast Ohio Chapter. She is also a member of Novelists Inc.

June's writing success earned her a place in the Hall of Fame at her alma mater, Mayfield High School in Mayfield, Ohio. She was also named "Woman of the Year" by the Western Reserve Business Woman's Association in 1993.

Her husband Charlie's illness, chronicled in *A Glass Full of Tears: Dementia Day-By-Day*, necessitated a break in her novel writing for more than two years. However, since Charlie was placed in a nursing home, June is once more back to her fiction writing.

In addition to her writing, June enjoys singing, flower arranging, and time with her family, which includes her daughters and sons-in-law, five grandchildren, and a great-grandson.